THE LOVING BRAND BOOK

THE LOVING BRAND BOOK

with an introduction by
CHARLES GOODNIGHT III

and illustrations by
WILLIAM D. WITTLIFF

1965 · THE PEMBERTON PRESS · AUSTIN

INTRODUCTION

When Charles Goodnight, Sr., died on December 12, 1929, I knew that an era had ended in the history of the Southwest. It was an era of individuals, of singular, colorful, hearty men—men who turned barren land into empires and then turned their absolute control into democracy. For they were men—the Lovings, the Slaughters, the Goodnights, and a dozen other families—who loved their freedom more than power. Only distantly related to the colonel, I nevertheless have the honor of bearing his name. He had no children of his own.

It has always seemed to me that the most important accomplishment of these men was not in carving cattle kingdoms out of the wilderness, supreme feat of heroism that it was, but that they would voluntarily give up the complete authority that they held over their land to form a democratic government. As I see it, the winning of the West was that two-fold transition, from wilderness to cattle kingdom, and from cattle kingdom to democracy and law. One of the beginnings of the second transition is the very manuscript published here.

The uses and advantages of branding stock are evident, but the crux of branding as a way of proving ownership is in knowing whose brand belongs to whom. Starting when Col. Goodnight and Oliver Loving were in their famous partnership, young James C. Loving—then still a young man—began the arduous task of compiling a list of all the brands and brand owners, with other vital information. After Oliver Loving died and the partnership dissolved, James Loving and Col. Goodnight still maintained a close friendship and close contact in forming their record of marks and brands. Then in the year 1877 Loving, grandfather, the Slaughters, and others founded the first cattleraisers association. One of the first functions was the protection of stock from theft, and their brand book took on double importance. More and more information was added, and finally by 1884 the task was as complete for that time as it ever would be. It is possible, in fact probable, that other copies of the handbook were made for the use of the stockmen's protective organization, but this copy is the only one known to exist. James Loving gave it to the Indian Agent, Col. John R. Ranson, at Fort Sill, Oklahoma, who used it to watch the cattle brought in by the Indians on the nearby reservation. Frequently he was able to spot thefts by the brands, and with the valuable Loving brand book to guide him was able to determine who the cattle belonged to and how to reach the owner to return them. Only recently the book turned up through Colonel Ranson's son, and is published here for the first time.

Since it was primarily James C. Loving who compiled the book, and since it is written in his hand, a short biographical sketch of his life is in order:

James C. Loving was born in Hopkins County, Kentucky, on June 6, 1836, the son of Oliver and Susan D. Loving. The family moved to Texas in 1845, stopping for awhile in Lamar County, then moving in 1846 to Collin County near the present town of Plano. At the age of twelve he began working for his father as teamster, driving ox-teams on freighting trips, some of which lasted as long as thirty or forty days. During the six years that he was on the road for his father, he was a "number one bull-whacker," as such drivers were known.

The family then moved in 1855 to what is now Palo Pinto County, settling in Loving Valley, known at the time as Pleasant Valley. Loving's father took James into partnership, naming the company O. Loving & Son. They gradually became interested in cattle and horse raising, selling at the time to the only near market, New Orleans. This was a good horse market but poor as far as beef was concerned. By the time of the Civil War they were the leading firm in their area.

James Loving joined the Confederate forces on ranger service, primarily in West Texas against Indian incursions. He commanded a company of 57 Texas Rangers. After the war he went into mercantile business at Weatherford, during which time his father and Col. Goodnight formed a partnership on an experimental cattle drive to New Mexico and Colorado, the famous Goodnight-Loving Trail being the result. The brands that they met up with as they went along were registered and retained for James C., who by this time had begun his record of marks and brands. Oliver Loving was wounded on the way to New Mexico by Indians, and died from the wounds at Ft. Sumner, New Mexico, in 1867. James went to the Colorado Territory to help grandfather with the remainder of the drive.

James Loving in 1868 gathered all the cattle owned by Loving & Goodnight and made an extremely hazardous drive to Colorado. The following is an account of that remarkable journey:

"To take a herd of cattle through from Texas to Colorado was then a hazardous undertaking, one in which even life had been lost, and as his father had been killed a year before in trying to do what J. C. Loving had now undertaken to do, was a matter of serious consideration to him. When everything was in readiness to start from Black Springs, in Palo Pinto County, he went home to tell his wife and little children (who were at Weatherford) good-by, for aught he knew for the last time. While he was gone, the Indians made a raid on the horse herd, near Black Springs, and took nearly all the horses that were to have been used in taking the herd of cattle through. Several days were taken up in getting

other horses, but finally, on the 20th day of June, 1868, the start was made from Black Springs, going by the northern route instead of the southern, as heretofore traveled by the Loving & Goodnight herds, in 1866 and 1867. The route was North, through the Indian Territory. There were some 1,500 head of cattle in the herd belonging to Loving & Goodnight, L. E. and Milton Ikard. Mode and Jno. Kutch, Fayette Wilson and Jno. H. Caruthers also had cattle in the herd. These were all cowboys who put their cattle in, and made hands themselves, to go through. Their bunches were small, and the herd aggregated, all told, about 2,300 head of cattle. There were two wagons loaded with provisions and camp equipage. The drive was made through the Indian Territory without special interruption or mishap and no trouble with the Indians was experienced in the Territory. Passing where Wichita, Kansas, now is, then a wilderness, with one company of United States soldiers camped there, they traveled up the Little Arkansas River to the old military road leading from Independence, Missouri, to Santa Fe, New Mexico, and took the west end of the road.

"Another herd of cattle had started from near Black Springs, immediately after and following the Loving & Goodnight herd. This herd was owned by Simpson Crawford, W. R. & J. C. Curtis and Chas. E. Rivers, all of whom were with the herd. In the Indian Territory, Jno. H. Caruthers cut out from the Loving & Goodnight herd and stopped, as also did Charley Rivers from the other herd. In Western Kansas, Crawford and the Ikard boys sold their cattle to J. C. Loving, for Loving & Goodnight, and the two herds were consolidated and numbered near 4,000 head of cattle. After this transaction, Crawford, the two Ikard boys and Henry Kutch (who was sick) returned to Texas. The balance of the two outfits was thrown together, and the drive West, on the old Santa Fe road, was continued under the management and control of J. C. Loving. When near the great bend of the Arkansas River and out on an open plain, the outfit was suddenly confronted by some 1,000 to 1,500 Indians mounted, and formed, to all appearances, in line of battle across the road some mile or more in front of the herd. Loving knew that he was in a country where the Comanche and the Kiowa Indians spent much of their time during the summer season, and the entire outfit realized that they were in the very jaws of death and gathered around their leader eagerly asking what was to be done to be saved. His instructions were for all of the men, twenty in number, to fall back to the wagons. When assembled there, they were told to get a good supply of cartridges from the wagon, as there were plenty and the men were all well armed, and to await the movements of the Indians, and if attacked to make the best fight that could be made under the circumstances, and sell out as dearly as possible, that there was no show to run and no place to which to run, the horses were jaded and in a bad condition to run, the Indians being mounted on good, fresh horses would soon kill them if they attempted to run, and that possibly if they presented a bold front and stood their ground, the Indians might not kill them. In a few minutes, three of the Indians left the main army and came to the cowboys, inquiring for their chief. Mr. Loving was pointed out to them and a conversation was had. One of the three Indians was a Comanche chief, by the name of Black Beaver, and another one was a Mexican. There was a man by the name of Calhoun in the cowboy outfit who talked the Mexican language; he and the Mexican did most of the talking and acted as interpreters. First, the Indian wanted to know if the cowboys were from Texas. As they (the Indians) were on the war-path with Texas, it would not do to admit that the outfit was from that country, so they were told that the men were not Texans, but were from Western Kansas, and had been down in the Cherokee Nation and had bought the cattle there, and that the cattle were for the Government, under contract. The chief then gave instructions that the cattle could go on, that they would not be interrupted. This was a great relief to the boys, as they had for the last half hour or more been expecting that their bones would be left on the plains to bleach.

"The Mexican said that some of the Indians, out killing buffalo, had discovered the herd and outfit a long distance off on the plains, and had taken them to be an army of Osage Indians, and that the Comanches were at war with the Osages, and that the 1,500 Indians that appeared in front of the cowboys had come out to give the Osages battle and not allow them to get to where their squaws and papooses were in camp, a few miles up the Arkansas River.

"The cattle were started on the trail again, and the main body of the Indians marched back up the river toward their camps. Several Indians, however, fell in with the cowboys, and traveled with them some distance, insisting that they must be Tehanas (which meant Texans). This, the boys stoutly denied, as they were confident that if their true identity became known to the Indians they would all be killed at once. An Indian who seemed hard to convince that the outfit was not from Texas, rode up by the side of W. H. Eddleman, one of the cowboys (now a banker in Weatherford, Texas,) and viewed him, his horse and rig very closely. Eddleman had a pair of rawhide hobbles around his horse's neck, which was very common in Texas, and these same Indians had cut many a pair of these hobbles off of horses in Texas and had driven the horses off. This Indian seemed to have a familiar knowledge of such hobbles, and looking into Eddelman's face, called him a d—n Tehana, and at the same time caught him by his somewhat prominent nose and gave it a decided twist. Eddleman, to all appearances, took this insult good-naturedly, as that was the only thing to do.

"The outfit camped that night near a large camp of the Indians and was not molested in the least. They traveled for several days up the Arkansas River, passing camps of Comanche and Kiowa Indians every day, saw large herds of horses owned by the Indians, many of which they had stolen from Texas, the brands being familiar to the boys. The drive was continued up the river to Fort Dodge; here they learned that the Cheyenne Indians were strictly on the war-path against everybody, and operating between Dodge and Fort Lyon, in Colorado, covering the route to be traveled by the cattle herd in order to reach its destination. Two or three days before the herd reached Dodge, the Cheyennes captured a mule train, freighting for the Government, forty-five miles above that place, and the excitement was running high. A good many wagon trains were on the road, hauling Government freight from down in Kansas or Missouri, to the Government Forts in New Mexico and Colorado. These trains were being stopped by the military at Dodge, on account of the Cheyenne Indians being on the war-path above there and depredating in the country through which these trains must pass. In a few days' time, more than 100 wagons had been stopped at Dodge; also, the Texas cattle herd and outfit had stopped to shelter under the wing of the military at Fort Dodge. The wagon bosses held a meeting in the Fort one day to decide what to do. The boss of the cattle herd joined in the meeting. It was found that there would be some 125 or 130 men altogether, with the wagon trains and the cattle outfit, so they decided to go through, provided the military officials would allow the freighters to make the attempt. The military officials of the Fort were then interviewed, and, after learning the strength of the outfit, agreed they might undertake to go through, but would not furnish any soldiers to guard them, as they were daily expecting the Indians to attack Fort Dodge, and would not allow any soldiers to leave for any purpose.

"It was some time in August when the wagon trains and the Loving and Goodnight herd left Fort Dodge, Kansas, for Fort Lyon, Colorado Territory, a distance of some 200 miles, and the entire route was through a wilderness and subject to be raided by the Cheyenne Indians at any time. The order of march was to double up the wagon trains, as there were two roads parallel with each other only a few yards apart all of the way, and the cattle herd traveled along the side of the wagon trains on the left or west side, and between the wagon road and the Arkansas River, as the road runs up the river all the way and is never far from the latter. Flank guards were kept out all the time, and in this way the outfit traveled the entire distance between the two military posts before mentioned without any serious accident or hindrance.

"Near Fort Lyon the wagon trains and cattle herds separated and bade each other good-by, as they were then past danger of the Indians, and felt greatly relieved. The drive from there to the Loving and Goodnight ranch, on the Apishapaw, in Colorado, was made without any trouble or accident, reaching there on the 14th day of September, 1868."*

Loving stayed in Colorado for three months and returned to Texas in January of 1869. He had married Mary E. Willett on January 15, 1857, having two sons and a daughter.

In 1870 Loving formed a partnership with Charles Rivers in Palo Pinto County, dividing the cattle at the end of the year, whereupon Loving ranched for awhile in Jack County, returning in 1871 to buy out Rivers, but on June 16, 1871, Rivers' camp was attacked by Indians with considerable loss, Rivers himself being wounded fatally. The transaction was completed, however, before Rivers' demise. Loving continued raising cattle in that area, having numerous engagements with the Indians. I have always thought it next to miraculous that James Loving, with all the numberless Indian fights and troubles with ornery hands, ever managed to come through it all alive. How those stories used to thrill me, and send chills down my spine!

It was in February of 1877 that long-time plans were finally culminated in the formation of the Texas Cattleraisers Association, first called the Cattle Raisers' Association of Northwest Texas. The principle founders were my grandfather, James Loving, and the Slaughters. Loving was elected secretary, a post which he held for twenty-five years. He also served as treasurer and general manager for several years. This association gradually brought an end to Indian depredations, range wars, and cattle rustling—and with those peace and democracy came to the range. It was no longer man against man, dog eat dog, but men working together with a common purpose.

James C. Loving, in addition to his work for the Cattleraisers Association, formed the Loving Cattle Company and managed it actively until 1892. He died in Fort Worth on November 24, 1902.

*Cox, James, *Historical and Biographical Record of the Cattle Industry and the Cattlemen of Texas and Adjacent Territory* (St. Louis: 1895), 346-50.

The early years of my life were full of visions of the old West and my eyes were big as plums when listening to the fascinating tales of Colonel Goodnight and the old cattlemen. That this book of brands should be published is a great source of satisfaction to me—it should serve as a useful and interesting guide to students of range history and the early days of the struggle to conquer the West. And to those whom J. Frank Dobie called "cow people," it should bring forth a flood of delightful memories of the good old days of the open range.

CHARLES GOODNIGHT III

Please take special good care of this Book and return Same to to me when done work

May 4th 1884

J. C. Loving
Jacksboro
Texas

Notice
"Abbreviations"

l	stands	for	Left
r	"	"	Right
s	"	"	Side
sh	"	"	Shoulder
h	"	"	Hip
th	"	"	Thigh
n	"	"	Neck
j	"	"	Jaw
e	"	"	Either
b	"	"	Both

"When the brand given is for Horses, or Mules the word Horses will be Written in Ear Mark Space

Ear Marks.	BRANDS.	NAME.	RANCHE.	POST OFFICE.
R B	A or N leff loin	Childress & Donnell Bros	Clear fork Brazos	Eliasville Young Co Texas
V m	A4	Hopson & Reynolds	Cherokee Mt BIT	Gainesville " "
	ALA.r.s.	Ewen, Small & Simson	Palo Pinto Co Tex	Palo Pinto " "
	ALE.r.s.	" " "	" " " "	" " " "
	B.r.s on.	Alamo Cattle Co	Clear fork Brazos	Fort Worth " "
Horses	B.sh or h.	" " "	" " " "	" "
	AG			
	AG	D. H. Philips	Hall. Co Texas	Valley View " "
	AG			
	AG			
	ATY	G. R. Jowell	Stonewall " " Anson Jones Co.	" "
	ALX.l.s.	H. H. McConnell	Jack " " Jacksboro	" "
	V.l.s. V.th	G. H. White	Greer " " " "	" "
	AMK			
	AN. AN.	Clay M. Mann	Kent & Borden " " Colorado City	" "
	A1			

5

Ear Marks.	BRANDS.	NAME.	RANCHE.	POST OFFICE.
⊘	A+	Culp. Dobkins & Co	Wichita Co Texas	Wichita Falls Texas
⊘	A. left side.	Joseph Campbell	Clay " "	Henrietta " "
⊘	A . side . ⎫			
⊘	AL " ⎬	Espuela Cattle Co	N.W. Texas	Fort Worth " "
⊘	AL " ⎭			
⊘	A ls ohip ⎫	C. F. Acers	Clay Co Texas	Henrietta " "
⊘	ARP. ls. ⎭	" "	" " "	" " "
⊘	A ⎫	Glidden & Sanbom	Potter & Randall	Houston " "
⊘	ΛV ⎭	For particulars	See Character brands	" "
⊘	ANA ls. ⎫			
⊘	ΛΝΛ ls. ⎬	W. B. Slaughter	Crosby. Co. Tex.	Dockums Ranche " "
⊘	ΛLY ls. ⎭			
⊘	ΛRT	Louisville Land & Cattle Co	King " "	Seymour " "
⊘	A lg. st flank	J. C. Loving	for particulars see brand under M heading	
⊘	ALL ⎫	M. O. Lynn	Stonewall Co Tex	Palo Pinto Texas
⊘	A♡.s. 75 hip ⎭	" "	" " " " "	" "

6

Ear Marks	BRANDS	NAME	RANCHE	POST OFFICE
(ear mark)	A h J s A sk	A. J. Addington	Chickasaw Nt B I T	Gainesville Texas
Horses (ear mark)	A left Sh.	Matthew Cartwright	Stonewall & Kaufman Co	Terrall "
(ear mark)	A D l. side	Geo. A. Scaling	Kent Co. Texas	Hubbard City "
(ear mark)	A S K }	Z. T. Addington	B I T	Gainesville "
(ear mark)	A	" " "	" "	" " "
(ear mark)	A N Either hip.			
(ear mark)	A N " " N. side.			
(ear mark)	A N " " Y R side.	A. P. Bush Jr	Scurry Co Tex	Colorado City " "
(ear mark)	A L l. low h.			
(ear mark)	A L low h.			
(ear mark)	A D l. side			
(ear mark)	A P. left hip.	Arlington Cattle Co	Nolan " "	Burnett "
(ear mark)	A P " side.			
(ear mark)	ΛΟΛ }	Matador Cattle Co	Bullard Springs	Fort Worth "
(ear mark)	A. A. A.	" "	" "	" " "
(ear mark)	A E. C &	J. N. Simpson	Baylor Co. Tex	Dallas "

7

Ear Marks	BRANDS	NAME.	RANCHE.	POST OFFICE.
	A—W.	C. C. Slaughter	Dallas Co Texas	Dallas Texas
	ΛN }	G. M. Casey	{ See character	Clinton Mo.
	Λ.ℓs. }	" "	for particulars	" "
	Λ. C.	J. N. Simpson	Baylor " "	Dallas Tex.
	Λ hips			
	Ā "	G. M. Casey		Clinton Mo
	AB. side	" "	{ For particulars	" "
	AU. hips	" "	See Character	" "
	AN. s. sh	" "	brands	" "
	ANT.	Curtis & Atkinson	Pan handle	Henrietta Texas
	ΛNΛ 0			
	ΛΛ Each or either side	Millsaps (Mid	Double	
	ΛΛ	Millikin	Mt. Fork	Colorado Texas
	Ʋ	J. J. Hittson	Brazos	Weatherford Ft
	A r.s.	W A Garner	Palo Pinto C.	Fort Worth "
	A Ms 44h	Mabry Slaughter & Crawford	Cattle Co.	Graham "

Ear Marks.	BRANDS	NAME.	RANCHE.	POST OFFICE.
⊙⊙	Λ Z l.s.	St Louis Cat Co		
⊙⊙	A·H l.s.	Chas Schunding	Lubbock Garza	St Louis Mo.
∞	AHHOH	Secy Treas	& Crosby Cos	
⊙∞	Z Z l.s. off	P.O. Room 22 Gay		
∞	Z l.s	building St Louis		
⊙∞	Z l.s			
⊙⊙	A h.s + ch	W H Yarbrough	A.T.	Spanish Fort T
⊙⊙	AB	Geo. H. Goddard		
∞				
∞				
∞				
∞				
∞				
∞				
∞				
∞				

9

Ear Marks.	BRANDS.	NAME.	RANCHE.	POST OFFICE.
⊙⊙	Ā rs + rsn / Ā	W. H. Yarbrough	Red River	Burlington Texas
⊙⊙ m				
∞	NW—	J. W. Simpson		Dallas "
∞	AB	Barra + Suggs	Denley Co.	Huntsville "
⊙⊙	Λ flours	C. M. Earley	Clay "	Henrietta "
∞				
∞				
∞				
∞				
∞				
∞				
∞				
∞				
∞				
∞				
∞				

Ear Marks.	BRANDS.	NAME.	RANCHE.	POST OFFICE.
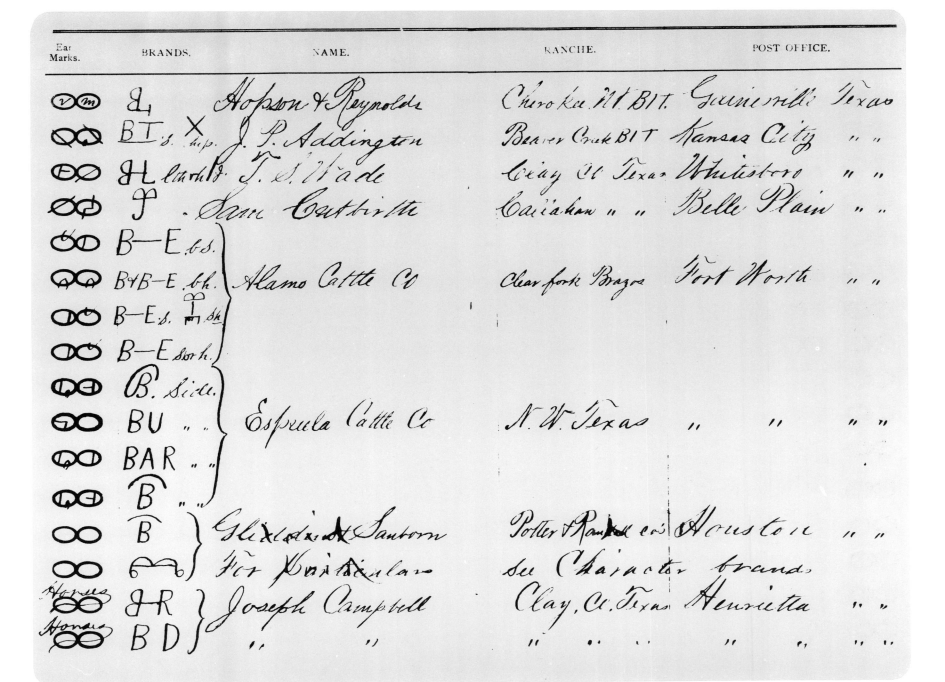	&,	Hopson & Reynolds	Cherokee Nt. B.T.	Gainesville Texas
	B.T. s. hip. X	J. P. Addington	Beaver Creek B.T.	Kansas City " "
	H clarkd.	T. S. Wade	Clay Co. Texas Whitesboro	" "
	S	Sam Catbirtte	Callahan " " Belle Plain	" "
	B—E. b.s.			
	B+B—E. b.h.	Alamo Cattle Co	Clear fork Brazos	Fort Worth " "
	B—E.s. sh.			
	B—E sb.h.			
	B. Side.			
	BU " "	Espuela Cattle Co	N. W. Texas " "	" "
	BAR " "			
	B " "			
	B	Glidden & Sanborn	Potter & Randall cos Houston	" "
		For Particulars	see Character brands	
Horses	H R	Joseph Campbell	Clay, Co. Texas Henrietta	" "
Horses	B D	" "	" " " "	" "

11

Ear Marks.	BRANDS.	NAME.	RANCHE.	POST OFFICE.
	BUS. es. de.	R. T. Davis	H... man Co Tex.	Valley View Texas
	BUS.. ∫ a	} 82 head Yearling steers	Sold to T. S. Hetten & 82 head 2 year old	
	BOZ. es.	rebranded 101 to George Miller	now held in B I T about 50 miles south of Hunnewell	
	BOON	Louisville Land & Cattle Co	King Co. Texa	Seymour Texas
	BEL es. ᴸth.	} J. C. Loving	Jack & Young Co "	Jacksboro " "
	BAR es. ?.	For particulars	See brands & under M. heading	
	∽ s. b. sides.	Dan Waggoner & Son	North Texas & B I T	Decatur " "
	⊍. Etter s.	W. A. Vinson	Choctaw M B I T	Gainesville " "
	B6 agar s.	} U. A. Jackson	Crosby Co Tex	Hillsboro " "
	B8 " s.	" " "	" " " "	" " " "
	BAB	John H. Stone	N. W. Texas	Gainesville " "
	⊍ es. F. W	Geo A. Scali...	Kent Co Texas	Hubbard City " "
	BOS	B. T. Addington	B I T	Gainesville " "
	B¥ es.	W. H. Williams	" "	Erin Springs B I T
	BER	A. P. Bush "	Scurry Co Texas	Colorado City Texas
	⊍	J. W. Reed	Camp Supply B I T	Fort Worth "

12

Ear Marks.	BRANDS.	NAME.	RANCHE.	POST OFFICE.
⊙⊙	BOB.	J. T. _____	Baylor _ Texas	Dallas Texas
⊙⊙	BL.	W. B. Worsham	Hardeman " "	Henrietta "
⊙⊙	BIL.	G. K. Elkins	Kent " "	Colorado City "
⊙⊙	BLAK.	C. C. Slaughter	Dallas " "	Dallas "
⊙⊙	BB. Side.	S. M. Casey		Clinton Mo.
⊙⊕	B. Side hip	" "	[For particulars	" "
⊙⊕	B. hip.	" "	see characters]	" "
⊙⊙	B. Side.	" "	brands	" "
⊙⊙	B6 r.s.	W. H. Yarbrough	Red River	Burlington "
∞	BAT.	Curtis & Atkinson	Panhandle	Henrietta Texas
∞				
∞				
∞				
∞				
∞				
∞				

13

Ear Marks.	BRANDS.	NAME.	RANCHE.	POST OFFICE.
	C ⊓ rh & s.	Red River Cattle Co	Clay Co Texas	Gainesville Texas
	CLC. chors	J. S. Wade	" " "	Whitesboro " "
	C D. rs.	}		
	C R T. rs.	} Geo. H. Goddard	Tom Green " "	St. Louis. Mo.
	C. rs & sh.	}		
	CLC. ls.	Kit Carter Cattle Co	Dickens & King " "	Seymour Texas
	C. & sh. T. s.	}		
Horses	C. l & sh. T. hip.	} J. S. & D. W. Godwin	Jones Co. " "	Fort Worth " "
	C. l sh. XF. s.	}		
Horses	C. l sh. XF. hip.	}		
	C. l sh. R hip.	} C. C. Rumrill	Knox " " "	Gainesville " "
Horses	C. left hip.	} " " "	" " " "	" " " "
	C. sh. S. Nh.	Louisville L & Cattle Co	King " " "	Seymour " "
	C O P ls	J. L. Hull	Clay " "	Secret Springs "
	C 2 rh & s.	" " "	" " " "	" " " "
	C	Z. T. Addington	B 1 T	Gainesville "

14

Ear Marks	Brands	Name	Ranche	Post Office
⊙⊙	C. &c. s. &c.			
⊙⊙	COE side			
⊙⊙	COE "			
⊙⊙	COW "	Espuela Cattle Co.	N. W. Texas	Fort Worth Texas.
⊙⊙	COC "			
⊙⊙	C P "			
⊙⊙	CU2	Glidden & Sanborn	For particulars see Character brands.	
⊙⊙	CCC &c.	C. W. B. Slaughter	Crosby Co Texas	Lockains Ranche, Texas.
⊙⊙	Ɔ	J. F. Evans	Donley " "	Sherman "
⊙⊙	CALL	W. E. Rayner	Knox " "	Seymour "
⊙⊙	CALL	" "	" " "	" "
⊙⊙	C S.	C. C. Slaughter	Colorado River	Dallas "
⊙⊙	C. X	G. M. Casey	{See Character	Clinton Mo
⊙⊙	CA	" "	for particulars} " " "	" " "
⊙⊙	CRO ⊤.	M. F. Ikard	Clay Co Texas	Henrietta Texas
⊙⊙	CS l side	G. M. Casey	See Character.	Clinton Mo

15

Ear Marks.	BRANDS.	NAME.	RANCHE.	POST OFFICE.
⊖⊖	CH hip			
⊖⊖	CH l.s. 9w	G. W. Casey		Clinton Mo
⊖⊖	CAl. side.		For particulars	
⊖⊖	)-T "		See Character	
⊖⊖	CX.		brands	
⊖⊖	CPS.	" "	" "	
⊖⊖	CA s. H.			
⊖⊖	CA s. H.			
⊖⊖	C4 lh hips behind acres			
⊖⊖	C4 lh hips behind acres 66	J. G. Boyd	Johnson Co.	Grand View Texas
Horses ⊖⊖	C4 l hip			
⊖⊖	COB l.s	B. R. Cobb	Clay Co.	Henrietta "
⊖⊖	CBr s.hip	C. C. Binkley	Grayson Co.	Sherman "
⊖⊖	CB l.s.			
⊖⊖	JK r.hrs.	L. S. Williams	J. T.	Spanish Fort "
⊖⊖	CLEO l.s.j. 73	Franklin L & C. Co.	Greer Co.	Donns

16

Ear Marks.	BRANDS.	NAME.	RANCHE.	POST OFFICE.
	Ch-sth	Millsap Milliken	Dbl. Mt. Fork	Colorado Texas
	S.L.hip	A. L. Butler	Clay Co.	Henrietta "
	C Olerh	C. M. Tilford	Crosby Co.	Colorado "
	CX	W. Scott Xiv	Harris	" "
	CΛLL³lsh	W. E. Rayner	King Co.	Seymour "
	CΛLL			
	C 4	Mallett Cat Co	Col River	Colorado City Tex
	CALᵈ lsh	S. J. Garvin	Washita R.	White Bear Hill I.T.

17

Ear Marks.	BRANDS.	NAME.	RANCHE.	POST OFFICE.
	DO. l.s. hip. DO.	Childress & Hommel Bro.	Clear fork Brazos	Eliasville Young co Texas
	DO. rt & side	" " "	" " "	" " "
	DATE s. DK.h. 60 n.	L. Hearne		Belle Plain "
	DIXN s. JM ts.	Moore & West.	King & Knox Co's Tex	Jackston "
	DSD. c side	L. S. Knead	Denton " Tex	Lewisville "
	DSD. l. side	" "	" " " " "	"
	Dor Dor D<	Adams & Holloway	Borden " "	Colorado City "
	DOX. side	Espuela Cattle Co	N. W. Texas	Fort Worth "
	DAN. " "	" " "	" " " "	"
	DAVE	Glidden & Sanborn	For particular see Character brands.	
	D. l.s. sn. hip.	J. K. Kuisdaster	Hood. Co Texas	Thorp Spring Texas
	D.r.h. 71.side. D.r.h. B.side. Horses D.l.sh. 71.neck.	Dan Waggoner & Son	North Texas & B.I.T	Decatur " "
	D. left side.	F. M. Hill	Collin. Co. Texas.	McKinney " "
	DA. side.	C. W. Wood	North Tex & B.I.T	Kansas City Mo.

18

Ear Marks.	BRANDS.	NAME.	RANCHE.	POST OFFICE.
⬭⬭	DNIS. r.s. C hip.	B. H. Dennis	Head Stephen Co	Branberry Texas
⬭⬭	DNIS. r.s. BIL hip.	" "	" " "	" " "
⬭⬭	D-N-D	J. W. Knox	Jack " Co	Jacksboro "
⬭⬭	DMD	" "	" " "	" " "
⬭⬭	DR	J. F. Reynolds	" " "	Roanoke "
⬭⬭	DX	J. W. Wilson	Concho " "	Gainesville "
⬭⬭	(D	G. M. Casey	{ See Characters	Clinton Mo
⬭⬭	(H		for particulars }	" " "
⬭⬭	DP. r.s. 3h. EA Ecot	A. A. Hillun	Archer Co Texas	Archer City Tex
⬭⬭	l.s OH hip.			
⬭⬭	l.s OH h. O.t		{ For particulars	
⬭⬭	l.s B. hip.	G. M. Casey	See Characters }	Clinton Mo
⬭⬭	A. hip.		brands }	
⬭⬭	left hip.			
⬭⬭	D/D	H. L. Vaden	Brinkum Creek BIT	Lebanon BIT
⬭⬭	D/D			

19

Ear Marks.	BRANDS.	NAME.	RANCHE.	POST OFFICE.
	DB ls across hip or brand	J. G. P. Boyd	Ellis Co.	Grand View Texas
	DB " " 53 m.			
	CK	J. R. Hudson	Nolan & Llano Cos.	Burnett "
	DΛ E hip	Glasgow Kinney & Co.	Young Co.	Graham "
	DB r. h.	J. B. Wilson	Concho "	Dallas "
	B rs. h.	Alamo Cat. Co.	Clear Fork of Brazos R.	Fort Worth "
Horses	B eh or L			
	D M s & H	Lexington Cattle Co	Ganzo Co	Fort Worth Tex
	D M side	J H Burgess Mang.		
	D ls bl th & Jaw	T. M. Hill	Collin Co	McKinney "
	DLΛ	W. A. Rodgers	Crosby Co	Dallas " "
	Dj Ls Nip Left side			

20

Ear Marks.	BRANDS.	NAME.	RANCHE.	POST OFFICE.
	E L A. r.s.	Ewen, Sikali & Simson	Palo Pinto Co Texas	Palo Pinto (box 34) Texas
	E H. l.s. P. hip.			
	E H. l.s. P. hip.	Catlett & Malin	Head Colorado River	Colorado City " "
	E H. side. P. hip.			
	E V A	Geo. A. Cooke	Stephens Co. Tex	Strawn " "
	E 7 Z	M. Ikard	Archer " "	Henrietta " "
	E. r.h. side. D.	G. H. White	Greer " "	Jacksboro " "
	Ð. Ð.	Clay. M. Haas	Kent & Borden " "	Colorado City " "
	E R C. side	Espuela Cattle Co	N. W. Texas	Fort Worth " "
	ℲⱢ	Louisville Land & Cattle Co	King Co. Texas	Seymour " "
	Ⓔ. r.s. r.h.	J. L. Hull	Clay " "	Secret Springs " "
	E T D. s. D.h.	" " "	" " "	" " "
	E P B	John H. Stone	N. W. Texas	Gainesville " "
	E	A. P. Bush Jr.	Scurry Co Tex	Colorado City " "
	E — J	J. N. Simpson	Bayer " "	Dallas "
	E R B	C. C. Slaughter	Colorado River	" "

21

Ear Marks.	BRANDS.	NAME.	RANCHE.	POST OFFICE.
∞	EJ	Morris & Brown		Gainesville Texas
∞	P. Side	G. M. Casey	See Characters	Clinton Mo
⦿⦿	EM	Millsap & Milliken	LH Mt Fork	Colorado Texas
⦿⦿	E l.s.h.	Even Small & Simson	Palo Pinto C.	Palo Pinto "
⦿⦿	E w. l.s.	W. S. Power	Fisher Co.	Sweetwater "
⦿⦿	st. Ɔ 4s	Sacra & Sugg	Denny "	Gainesville "
∞	ΈOᵉˢ Oᵉⁿ	Lexington Car Co.	Garza Co	Fort Worth Tex
⦿⦿	ESDs	H. H. McConnell	Jack Co	Jacksboro "
∞				
∞				
∞				
∞				
∞				
∞				
∞				
∞				

22

Ear Marks.	BRANDS.	NAME.	RANCHE.	POST OFFICE.
	7 point L side	J. W. Book	Garza. Co. Texas	Fort Worth Texas
	FO. R.s & th	Geo. H. Goddard	Tom Green " "	St Louis. Mo.
	F. l.s & hip.	Kit Carter Cattle Co	Dickens & King " "	Seymour Texas
	FOS. l.side	Ewen Small & Simson	Palo Pinto " "	Palo Pinto (box 34) "
	FWS. side	Alamo Cattle Co	Clear fork Brazos	Fort Worth "
	F l.s & hip	}		
	F. l.s & loin	W. B. Slaughter	Crosby. Co Texas	Dockums Ranche Texas
	F l.s & hip			
	F.F. l.s. loin &c	}		
	F—M F }	Frey & Millican	Erath " "	Stephensville " "
	FRY }	" "	" " "	" " " "
	l.s. Fh 60 m	H. O. Bedford	Knox " "	Seymour " "
	FORD }	Louisville L. & Cattle Co	King " "	" " " "
	L	" " " "	" " "	" " " "
	F+F }	John Flint	Young. "	Fort Worth " "
	F+F }	" "	" " "	" " " "

23

Ear Marks.	BRANDS.	NAME.	RANCHE.	POST OFFICE.
∞	FILES	C. W. Ward	North Texas BIT	Kansas City. Mo.
∞	F T. es. F hun			
∞	F T. es.	G. W. William	Pecos River	Dallas. Texas
∞	F. left side			
∞	F es			
∞	FEN es. +	J. Norman Fenton	Sweetwater Crk Tx	Sweetwater " .
∞	FARD. es.	A. P. Bush Jr	Scurry Co Tex	Colorado City " .
∞	FARD. es. EF left	" "	" " " "	" " " "
∞	FC. FC.	J. N. Simpson	Baylor " "	Dallas "
∞	FLH.	Mabry. Glasgow & Crawford	Cottle " "	Graham "
∞	FIX. eh	M. F. Ikard	Clay " "	Henrietta "
∞	FA. h & s.			
∞	FH. h & s.	Sam Lazarus.	King & Hickm " "	Seymour "
∞	FEW. "			
∞	FA ls.	L. B. Gardner	" " " "	Albany "
∞	FEW ls.			

24

Ear Marks.	BRANDS.	NAME.	RANCHE.	POST OFFICE.
	FR			
	FRh +sh			
	FRh +sh	J. R. Hudson	Nolan & Llano Cos.	Burnett, Texas
	FRh +sh	Arlington Cat.	Co. 1	
	FR h +sh			
	FOX r.s.	Glasgow Causey & Co.	Young Co.	Graham "
	Frsh. o. rh			
	Fls.rh	Franklin L. & C. Co.	Greer Co.	Doans "
	F " "			
	F r.s. rsh.	J. H. Nail	I.T.	Caddo I.T.
	F rh.rs	N & his cattle	in this brand	
	FC rsrh	Martin Colbert	I.T.	Eran Springs "
	FAT	Lexington Cat Co	Garza Co	Ft Worth

25

Ear Marks.	BRANDS.	NAME.	RANCHE.	POST OFFICE.
	GB cs. Thigh.	A. B. Roff	Chickasaw. Nt. Bit.	Gainesville Texas
	GB " Sh.	"	" " "	"
	GED cs Espuela Cattle Co.	N. W. Texas	Fort Worth . "
Horse	GM	Joseph Campbell	Clay Co "	Henrietta "
	GS cowhip.	Geo. A. Scaling	Kent " "	Hubbard City "
	GUS.	Matador Cattle Co	Ballard Spring	Fort Worth "
	GNG cs.	N. R. Fullton	Archer Co Texas	Archer City "
	GNG cs.	"	" " " " "	"
	GNE hip.	G. M. Casey	See Character.	Clinton Mo.
Horses	GWW sh.	G. W. Williams	Pecas River	Lookout N. M.
	GEL vs.	L. B. Gardner	Dickens & King Cos	Albany Texas
	GH vs sh.	Glasgow Causey & Co.	Young Co	Graham "
	GTH cs.			
	G vs sh.	A. J. Addington	I. T.	Gainesville "
	G . "			

Ear Marks.	BRANDS.	NAME.	RANCHE.	POST OFFICE.
⊘⊘	Ⓗ .ℰ.s. H.sh.	Red River Cattle Co	Clay Co Texas	Gainesville Texas
⊘⊘	HAIL .l.s.	" " " "	" " " "	" " "
⊘⊘	HIL .s. I .th.	Hopson & Reynolds	Cherokee. N. BIT	" " "
⊘⊘	I .Side.	" " "	" " " " "	" "
⊘⊘	AA .left. Side	T. S. Wade	Clay Co. Tex.	Whitesboro "
⊘⊘	H .left jaw.	J. T. Hill	Palo Pinto " "	Weatherford "
⊘⊘	200 head sold to Aleck Moore, rebranan		OK.ℰ.s. L.th. & now held in Palo Pinto co. "	
⊘⊘	H .sh. s.rtt	W. P. Harmonson	Denton Co. Tex.	Roanoke, Denton Co. Texas
⊘⊘	H.OP	G. R. Jowell	Stonewall " "	Anson, Jones " " "
⊘⊘	HIK .l.s.rtt.	A. H. Henson	Jack " "	Jacksboro " "
⊘⊘	HIK .l.s H.hip	62. head 3 yr old steers.	sold in June 1863 to B. W. Cott	
⊘⊘	HIK .ℰ.s. sored have it on thigh	they were rebranded	on one side & on the other, & are now held	
⊘⊘	HIK {bought Cattle}	in Cotts Pasture.	Archer co Texas,	
⊘⊘	HX .side.			
⊘⊘	HO ..	Espuela Cattle Co.	N. W. Texas	Fort Worth Texas
⊘⊘	HV ..			

27

Ear Marks.	BRANDS.	NAME.	RANCHE.	POST OFFICE.
∞	HN. HN.	Clay. McMann	Kent & Borden co. Tex. Colorado City	Tex
∞	HIX (Double Hawe Has) rs.	C. F. Acers	Clay co „ Henrietta	„
∞	H. l.s. }	Gliddon & Sanborn	Potter & Randall cos Houston	„
∞	HUD }			
∞	H	two last brands tougher of	Acers or Witherspoon (see Characters)	
∞	HSD l.s. hip }	W. B. Slaughter	Crosby Co Texas Dockums Ranche	„
∞	HSD l.s. C hip }	„ „ „ „	„ „ „ „ „ „ „ „	„
∞	H H Louisville Land & Cattle Co	King „ „ Seymour	„
∞	HAT l.s. G. j. }			
∞	HAT l.side	J. C. Loving	Jack & Young „ „ Jacksboro	„
∞ Horses	HAT l. hip }	For particulars	See brands under its heading	„
∞	HIT. Either S. }			
∞	HIT. „ „	Hittson & Reed	Stonewall & Fisher cos Weatherford	„
∞ Horses	HIT l.shor. h }			
∞	H s.r.h. & l.h.	J. L. Hull	Clay Co. Tex. Secret Springs	„
∞	HOT	Dan Waggoner & Son	North Texas & Bit Decatur	„

28

Ear Marks.	BRANDS.	NAME.	RANCHE.	POST OFFICE.
	H sh. S, hip,	F. M. Hill	Collin Co Texas	McKinney Texas
	H—L. side.	L. L. Tackitt	Young " "	Graham " "
	H sh. W. s. }	D. W. Barnett	Tom Green " "	Dallas " "
	H sh W. s.	" " "	" " " "	" " " "
	HOT	Z. T. Adelington	B I T	Gainesville " "
	H. rs rh. }	J. M. McKenzie	Kent Cl Tex	Colorado City " "
	HALL }	" " "	" " "	" " " "
	H lsh. Ts. H hip	W. H. Williams	B I T	Erin Springs B Tex
	H sh. I side	" "	"	" " B I T
	HOO E sor h.	Guildford McCulla co	Hardeman. Co. Tex	Gainesville Texas
	HXW. s. }			
	H. s th.	Arlington Cattle. Co.	Nolan. Co. Texas.	Burnett "
	H. lor b s. }	1500 arico in 1881 to	J W Taylor & driven to pasture in La Salle Co	
Horses	H. 6 th.			
	H. hip. }	E. C. Peery.	Cooke " "	Gainesville "
	H. " }			

29

Ear Marks.	BRANDS.	NAME.	RANCHE.	POST OFFICE.
⊘⊘	HX.	J. M. Jones.	Clay. Co. Texas	Riverland Texas.
⊘⊘	HW.			
⊘⊘	HW. }	J. N. Simpson	Baylor „ „	Dallas „
⊘⊘	HW			
⊘⊘	ß }	J. D. Reed	Camp. Supply B.T.	Fort Worth „
⊘⊘	H }	„ „	„ „ „	„ „ „
⊘⊘	HOY	Curtis & Atkinson	Panhandle	Henrietta „
⊘⊘	I l.sh. }	S. P. Reynolds	Jack Co Tex	Roanoke „
⊘⊘	I „ }	„ „	„ „ „	„ „
⊘⊘	H s. r.h. }	C. C. Slaughter	Dallas „ „	Dallas „
⊘⊘	HU h. + s. }	„ „	„ „ „ „	„ „
∞	HEX. }	Matador Cattle Co	Ballard Springs	Fort Worth „
∞	H— }	„ „ „	„ „ „ „	„ „
⊘⊘	HX }	G. M. Casey	{ See Characters for particulars }	Clinton Mo
⊘⊘	HOL. ʲʰ	„ „	„ „	„ „ „
∞	H sh. Sth.	J. N. Simpson	Baylor Co Tex	Dallas Texas

Ear Marks.	BRANDS.	NAME.	RANCHE.	POST OFFICE.
∞	H E S. l.s. C. Jan.	J. W. Corn	Tarrant Co Tex	Bear Creek Texas
∞	H E S. (sor toin)	" "	" "	" "
∞	HID.	Sam Lazarus	King & Dickens " "	Sherman Seymour "
∞	H.	Morris & Brown		Gainsville "
∞	H 2. Jan.	" "	"	" " "
∞	HIK. eth.	A. C. Hanson	Jack. Co Tex.	Jacksboro "
∞	H I. ethip	N. H. Williams	BIT	Erin Spring BIT
∞	HB. side		(For particular	
∞	H "	G. M. Casey	see other character	Clinton Mo.
∞	H 3. f Jan		brands	
∞	H I l.s.	Wm Hudson	Cook Co.	Gainsville Texas
∞	HB ether ＋H j.	B W Rickit	Clay & Co.	Henrietta "
∞	HSE l.s.	Glasgow Causey & Co.	Young Co.	Graham "
∞	H ＋	Odem & Collins	Knox "	Henrietta "
∞	HC. H ▫ 5	Franklin L & C Co.	Greer "	Doans "
∞	H ▷	Curtis & Atkinson	Panhandle	Henrietta "

31

Ear Marks.	BRANDS.	NAME.	RANCHE.	POST OFFICE.
∞	HOL l.s.	W. B. Gardner	Dickens ma.	Albany, Texas
∞	HOL "		King Co.	
⊕B	H left limb	J. T. Hill,	Palo Pinto Co.	Weatherford "
∞	H r.s. H r.h. H r.sh.			
∞	HTC l.s.	W. S. Power	Fisher Co.	Sweetwater "
Vm	H n. H r.s.			
⊕m	H r.i. sh. H r.i.s.			
∞	H l. hip			
∞	H " "	W. A. Garner	Palo Pinto Co.	Fort Worth "
∞F	I l.s.h.			
∞	I " "			
∞	HUL l.s.	J. D. Hull	Clay Co	Henrietta "
Vn	HUL " "			
∞	H Ho H l.s.	St Louis Cat Co	Lubbock Garga & Crosby Co.	No 22 Gay Bldng St Louis Mo.
∞	HO l.s "	Chas Schunking		
∞B	HOS l.s	Kuy Brean		
HOT	HOT. AG	Mallen Cat Co	Col River	Col City Tex

32

Ear Marks.	BRANDS.	NAME.	RANCHE.	POST OFFICE.
	1OU ℓs.	T. S. Wade	Clay Co Texas	Whitesboro Texas
	1J. 8th.	Alamo Cattle Co	Clear fork Brazos	Fort Worth "
	1SL	" " "	" " "	" " "
	IVΛ			
	IVΛ			
	IVΛ	M. Ikard	Archer Co Texas	Henrietta " "
	IKARD			
	IKARD			
	1X. side	Espuela Cattle Co	N.W. Texas	Fort Worth "
	1K. "	" " "	" "	" " " "
	1S. Lt th.			
	1S. " "	E. C. Sugg & Bro.	Beaver Creek B I T	Gainesville " "
Horses	1S. th th.			
Horses	1Sh. "so. th. α n.			
	1M	Frey & Millican	Erath Co Texas	Stephensville Texas
	1CO. ℓs.	Norman Fenton	Head of Sweetwater	Sweetwater "

33

Ear Marks.	BRANDS.	NAME.	RANCHE.	POST OFFICE.
	IIX. &&.	T. H. Wilson & Bro	Montague Co Texas	Spanish Fort. Texas.
	IZL	J. D. Reed	Camp Supply. I.T.	Fort Worth "
	ISH &&.	W. B. Worsham	Hardeman Co Tex	Henrietta "
	IXL	Curtis & Atkinson	Panhandle "	" " "
	IB. }	Morris & Brown		Gainesville "
	IV. V. }	" "		" "
	IX2. Tjaw.	D. E Ball	Cooke Co Texas	" "
	IT hip			
	IT. " }	G. M. Casey	(See Characters	Clinton Mo
	ID " }		for particulars)	
	INK_Th	Mataan L & C. Co	Motley Co	Fort Worth Texas
	IS_IS_IS			
	IS ⌒			
	IS_IS }	E. C. Sugg & Bro	J. T.	Gainesville "
	IS.IS			
	IS.IS			

Ear Marks.	BRANDS.	NAME.	RANCHE.	POST OFFICE.
∞	IXL			
∞	IXK	Curtis and	Pan Handle	Henrietta Texas
∞	IVI	Atkinson		
∞	IX2			
∞	IW	Lexington Cat Co	Targa Co	Fort Worth Tex
∞	1Z	Mallett Cat Co	Col River	Colorado City "
∞	1Y	Jno. M. Hamilton	Chick Nat	Gainesville Tex
∞	1Y1			
∞				
∞				
∞				
∞				
∞				
∞				
∞				

Ear Marks.	BRANDS.	NAME.	RANCHE.	POST OFFICE.
⊙⊙	JFB. ls. JFa. }	Red River Cattle Co	Clay Co Texas	Gainesville Texas
⊙⊙	JES. Es. JEa. }	" " " "	" " "	" " "
⊙⊙	E lssh.	Joseph Benedict	Young " "	Belknap "
⊙⊙	JSC. ls.	Kit Carter Cattle Co	Dickens & King " "	Seymour "
⊙⊙	JS. es. }	A. B. Ross	Chickasaw Nt Ivt	Gainesville "
⊙⊙ Horse	A sh both	" "	" " " "	" " "
⊙⊙	JOLY. ls.	Owen Small & Stinson	Palo Pinto Co Tex	Palo Pinto (Texas) "
⊙⊙	JL. +2. Sico. JL esp.	Alamo Cattle Co	Clear fork Brazos	Fort Worth "
⊙⊙	JMD }	" " "	" " " "	" " "
⊙⊙	JOEL }			
⊙⊙	JOEL }	G. R. Jowell	Stonewall co Tex	Anson Jones Co. " "
⊙⊙	JOEL }			
⊙⊙	J— }	A. L. Hinson	Jack Co Texas	Jacksboro " "
⊙⊙	J—B }	" "	" " " "	" " "
⊙⊙	JCM & IC }	Clay. M. Mann	Kent & Borden " "	Colorado City " "
⊙⊙	JK }	" "	" " " "	" " "

36

Ear Marks.	BRANDS.	NAME.	RANCHE.	POST OFFICE.
◐◐	H. Sh.			
◐◐	JXH Side.			
◐◐	AM "			
◐◐	JM " Ch			
◐◐	JRG "			
◐◐	JTU "	Espuria Cattle Co.	N. W. Texas	Fort Worth Texas.
◐◐	JMH "			
◐◐	J2 "			
◐◐	J2 "			
◐◐	JK "			
◐◐	JAB "			
◐◐	JC sh. Hs.			
◐◐	H or H. ls.	C. F. Acers	Clay Co Texas	Henrietta "
◐◐	JWH. ls.			
◐◐	JWC. ls.	H. G. Bedford	Knox "	Seymour "
◐◐	JWC. ls.	" " "	" " "	" "

37

Ear Marks.	BRANDS.	NAME.	RANCHE.	POST OFFICE.
∞	JH	Glidden & Sanborn	For particulars see Character brands.	
∞	JAW. Es.	R. T. Curtis	Hardeman Co. Tex.	Valley View Texas
∞	JC	Barefoot & Bryant	Chickasaw Nt. Bit	Montague " "
Horses ∞	JOC Either	Joseph Campbell	Clay Co. Tex.	Henrietta " "
Horses ∞	J & R —	" "	" " " "	" "
∞	JWL Ls.	J. C. Loving	Jack & Young " "	Jacksboro " "
∞	JC. Ls. L. th.	For particulars	See brands under M. heading.	
∞	C Liver & th.			
Horses ∞	C Loin & th. Lth.	Hittson & Reed	Stonewall & Fisher cos	Weatherford " "
∞	C H Ls. H hip.			
∞	JIM. Ls.	G. W. Wolcott	Tom Green " Tex	Big Spring " "
∞	J. Either side.	W. G. Vinson	Choctaw. Nt. Bit	Gainesville " "
∞	JAC	J. A. Carroll	Denton Co. Tex	Denton " "
Horses ∞	JF. Sh. & th.	John Flint	Young " "	Fort Worth " "
∞	JHJ. Ls.	P. C. Harmonson & Bro	Archer " "	Farmer " "
∞	JHJ. Ls.	" " "	" " " "	" "

38

Ear Marks.	BRANDS.	NAME.	RANCHE.	POST OFFICE.
⊗⊗	J.C. [brand]	J. C. Lindsey	For particulars see O C T brand	
⊗⊗	JOH	W. Scott	Colorado & Pecos River	Colorado City Texas
⊗ ⊘	JJ			
⊘⊘	ЯЯ	A. P. Bush Jr.	Scurry Co Texas	" " "
⊘⊘	ЯЯ			
∞	A. [r.s.]			
⊗⊘	JP	W. E. Rayner	Knox " " Seymour "
⊗⊘	J+.			
⊗⊘	J+	J. D. Reed	Camp Supply 30 T	Fort Worth "
⊗∞	J+			
⊗⊗	JON. S.	J. B. Slaughter	Crosby Co Tex	Dockums Ranch "
⊗⊗	F sh. 1 th			
⊙∞	JHF			
⊙∞	JIZ	Mabry. Glasgow	Cottle " " Graham "
⊙∞	JOZ	& Crawford		
⊗⊗	F. hip.			

39

Ear Marks.	BRANDS.	NAME.	RANCHE.	POST OFFICE.
	JON. JON.	S. F. Reynolds	Jack. Co. Texas	Roanoke Texas
	JD	J. F. Edwards	Denton " "	Sherman "
	B. A.	C. C. Slaughter	Dallas " "	Dallas "
	JS. w.	J. H. Stradley	Jack " "	Jacksboro "
	JOW. Es.	Catherine L. & Cattle Co	Henderson " "	Gainsville "
	JE—.es.	For particular	see Figure brands	
	JL. esk.	J. N. Simpson	Baylor co Tex.	Dallas "
	JHU.	Sam Lazarus	King & Dickens " "	Seymour "
	JP. 5th. Jaw.			
	JL. hip.			
	JHL. side			
	JV. hip	G. M. Casey	For particulars see Character brands	Clinton Mo
	J Side			
	JCB ..			
	JZ. hip.			
	Hlhrs	A. L. Butler	Clay Co.	Henrietta Texas

Ear Marks.	BRANDS.	NAME.	RANCHE.	POST OFFICE.
		J. Hitson		
⊙ m	JOLY B	William End	Dbl. Mt. Fork Colorado Texas	
v m	Chs. rsh	Milliken	f Brazos R. Weatherford Tx	
v m	JC l.s. rh.	J. C. Carpenter	Wise C. Decatur "
H v	JC lsh.			
∞	J7	J. R. Hudson	Nolan m Llano Co's Burnett "
∞	JM	Arlington Cat. Co.		
∞	J+			
∞	J+ U e.s.	Hawkins Serar & Byler	Pecos River Ft. Worth & Kansas City
∞	J+ ♥ e.s.	150 head sold	out of J+ U _ J+ ♥ J‡ PEL End
∞	J5 & RB.	✳ brands to W	L. Cheeker Seymour Texas
v m	JM & RB.	void		
∞	JV l.s. rh.	J. B. Wilson	Concho Co. Dallas "
∞	JVJ l.s.			
∞	J Fls rh	Franklin L & C. Co.	Iron Co. Howes "
∞	JO ls.	W. S. Power	Fisher " Sweetwater "
∞	J66 r.s.	W. W. Garner	Palo Pinto " Fort Worth "

41

Ear Marks.	BRANDS.	NAME.	RANCHE.	POST OFFICE.
⊙⊙	JON Ls.		Oil Springs	
⊙⊙	J5 r.s.		Prairie	
∞ ○	Ish. Whit	J. C. Washington	Chickasaw	Gainesville Texas
⊙⊙	JW any when		Nation	
H∞○	Ish. Wheeli		I.T.	
∞ ○	N Steer cattle	J. H. Nail	I.T.	Caddo I.T.
∞ ○	Ns Cth	J. N. Simpson		Dallas Texas
∞ ○	JO			
∞ ○	JOs	Sacra & Suggs	Wonley Co	Gainesville "
∞ ○	JO			
∞ ○	Hrsth.	Crospus Embree & figgn White	Greer Co.	Graham "
⊙⊙	JC s+H	Lexington Cat Co	Garza Co	Fort Worth Tex
⊙⊙	JUL	W. H. Yarborough	B.I.T.	Spanish Fort Tex
∞ ○				
∞ ○				
∞ ○				

42

Ear Marks.	BRANDS.	NAME.	RANCHE.	POST OFFICE.
	K behind sh. L dia. ∧ th	Kimberlin Cattle Co	Spur Co & BIT	Sherman Texas
	K „ L „ + th	„ „ „ „	„ „ „ „ „ „	„ „ „
	KIT side O h.	J. P. Addington	Beaver Creek „	Kansas City. Mo.
	KEN. ls. 2 sh	Joseph Benedict	Young Co Texas	Belknap. Texas.
	K. Sth.	Espuela Cattle Co	N. W. Texas	Fort Worth „ „
	KIL side	„ „ „	„ „ „ „ „ „	
	K. F. ls.	J. W. Mooar Bros	Scurry. co „	Colorado City „ „
	KOB ls.	B. R. Cobb	Clay Co.	Henrietta „
	KOB „	see Figures	for particulars	
	K side	Glasgow Causey Co.	Young Co.	Graham „
	KIN s O J.	G. K. Elkins	Kent „	Colorado „
	KMP ls.	W. S. Power	Fisher „	Sweetwater „
	KID	St Louis Cat Co.	Lubbock Gar Bros	No 223 Gay blding St Louis
	KID	„	„	„ + „

43

Ear Marks.	BRANDS.	NAME.	RANCHE.	POST OFFICE.
	⌐X }	W. S. Skurd	Archer Co Texas	Henrietta Texas
	⌐X }	" " "	" " "	" " "
	⌐ side }			
	⌐	L. Hearne		Belle Plain "
	L.H hip }			
	L.H			
	L·OS. l.s. }	D. H. Sweeney	Jack " "	Gertrude Jack Co "
	LOS. l.s. }	" "	" " "	" " "
	LLL 9. l.s. }	S. B. Burnett	Wichita " "	Fort Worth "
	L under tit C Bar left sh. }	Some LLL 9 steers included	in 6666 sale to Guinan King & Dickens cos. Tex	Montgomery co
	⌐ l.s.h.	Kit Carter Cattle Co		Seymour Texas
	LS +2 l.s. ·LS.h	Alamo Cattle "	Clear fork Brazos	Fort Worth " "
	LAN side 9	Clay M. Mann	Kent & Borden cos	Colorado City " "
	4 side }	Espuela Cattle Co	N W Texas	Fort Worth " "
	LED " }	" " "	" "	" " "
	LXS l.s.	C. F. Acers	Clay Co "	Henrietta " "

44

Ear Marks.	BRANDS.	NAME.	RANCHE.	POST OFFICE.
∞	L L	Glidden & Sanborn	for particular see character brands.	
∞	LYON. r.s.	R. T. Harris	Hardaman. Co. Tex.	Valley View Texas
∞	L cs. S.nock	H. V. Bedford	Knox " "	Seymour "
∞	LIL			
∞	LIL			
∞	LAL	M. O. Lynn	Stonewall " "	Palo Pinto " "
∞	L			
∞	LIX			
∞	LL side.	Lindsay Bedford & Hinton J. M. Lindsay	Benjamin Cooke " "	Fort Gainesville " "
∞	LIKE. side.	L. L. Jackitt	Young " "	Graham " "
∞	LN	A. P. Bush Jr	Scurry " "	Colorado City " "
∞	LUE	J. W. Knox	Jack " "	Jacksboro " "
∞	LUC. s.	Arlington. Cattle. co.	Nolan " "	Burnett "
∞	LIP. s.	" " "	" " "	" "
∞	LIZ	Matador " "	Ballard Springs	Fort Worth "
	Γ. ◊	J. D. Reed	Camp Supply BIT	" " "

45

Ear Marks.	BRANDS.	NAME.	RANCHE.	POST OFFICE.
	<u>LIN</u>			
	LIN	W. E. Rayner	Knox. Co. Texas	Seymour. Tex.
	LIN			
	LAZ	Curtis & Atkinson	Panhandle	Henrietta "
	LM	C. C. Slaughter	Colorado River	Dallas "
	LA	G. M. Casey	See Character	Clinton Mo.
	L77	Sam Lazarus	King & Dickens Cos. Tex	Sherman Seymour Tex
	LL side.			
	L6 "	G. M. Casey	See Characters	Clinton Mo
	L6 "		for particulars	
	NB			
	LMS =m			
	LMs	Sacra & Bugg	Donley Co.	Gainesville Texas
	LL ls LH			
	LL ls.	L. S. Williams	I. T.	Spanish Ft. I. T.
	L ls.			
	LL lh.			

46

Ear Marks.	BRANDS.	NAME.	RANCHE.	POST OFFICE.
	LOV r.s. SL	W. B. Gardner	Dickens and King Cos.	Albany, Texas
	LOV r.s. SL			
	— L l.s.	J. H. Lunay	Kent "	Colorado "
	L l.h.	J. B. Wilson	Concho	Dallas "
	L + □	Millsap & Milliken	Dbl. Mt. Fork	Colorado "
	L l.s. l.s. m.h.	Wichita & Brazos Stock Ass.	Knox Co.	Benjamin "
	LIZ l.s.	T. B. Ellison	Childress Co.	Kirkland "
	LIZ l.s. c.m.h.			
	L Hs 4 h	J. L. Hull	Clay Co.	Scent Springs "
	L O S es	W. B. Sweeney	Jack "	Gertrude "
	LOS l.h. m.h.			
	LAS	Curtis & Atkinson	Panhandle	Henrietta "
	LK			
	LA s.h.	Glasgow Currey & Co.	Young Co.	Graham "
	L 4	J Mallett Cat Co.	Col River	Colorado City "
	LET o O h			

Ear Marks.	BRANDS.	NAME.	RANCHE.	POST OFFICE.
	M.ls.thp.	Jasper McCoy.	Callahan Co Tex	Belle Plain Texas
	M.h.s+n.		" " "	" " "
	MORE.s. h.	Curtis & Atkinson	King & Knox " "	"Henrietta "Tex
	MOON	Moore & West	Head Colorado River	Jacksboro " "
	MOON	Catlett & Malin	" " " "	Colorado City " "
	M.ch+S.	" "	Jack Co Texas	" " "
	MRB.s. h.	H. H. McConnell	" " "	Jacksboro " "
	M. .K	" " "	Kent & Borden " "	" " "
	MOL.s. K.	Clay. M. Mann		Colorado City " "
	MAP "			
	MOK "	Espuela Cattle. Co.	N. W. Texas	Fort. Worth " "
	MAX "			
	MOB "			
	M bs. th.	R. T. Davis	Hardeman Co Tex	Valley View " "
	M+D.Es.	For particulars	see BWS brand.	
	M & L	Joseph Campbell	Clay. Co. Texas	Henrietta " "

Ear Marks.	BRANDS.	NAME.	RANCHE.	POST OFFICE.
⊖⊖	MAY. L.S. ▢ R.	J. C. Loving	Jack & Young Cos. Tex	Jacksboro Texas
⊖⊖	RIEL. L.S.			
⊖⊖	MEL. L.S.	There was sold out of	these & other brands belonging to the Loving	
⊖⊖	MOR. L.S. E R.	Cattle company	for the purpose of being fed last winter.	
⊖⊖	MOT. L.S. M R.	110 Steers in Sept 1883	to Jas Clymer of Collin Co Texas. &	
⊖⊖	MOT. Left hip	300 " " Oct & Nov "	" Turner Lancaster & Co, Hood Co Tex	
⊖⊖	MOT. Either S.			
⊖⊖	MAY. L.th)			
⊖⊖	MED. E.S.	Hitson & Reed	Stonewall & Fisher Cos	Weatherford. Texas.
⊖⊖	WEJ. right side	W. A. Jackson	Crosby Co. Tex	Hillsboro "
⊖⊖	M left side	W. F. Lewis	Tom Green " "	Colorado City "
⊖⊖	M " "	" " "	" " " "	" " " "
⊖⊖	MC. L.S.	G. W. Williams	Pecos River	Dallas "
⊖⊖	MAT. R.S.	Matthew Cartwright	Stonewall & Kaufman Cos	Terrell "
⊖⊖	MAN	A. P. Bush Jr	Scurry. Co. Tex	Colorado City "
⊖⊖	M	" " "	" " " "	" " " "

49

Ear Marks.	BRANDS.	NAME.	RANCHE.	POST OFFICE.
	MH ls.	J. M. McKenzie	Kent Co Texas	Colorado City Texas
	MYRS. ls.	Arlington Cattle Co	Nolan " "	Burnett "
	M ls. Vth.	J. N. Simpson	Baylor " "	Dallas "
	⚡M⚡	C. C. Slaughter	Colorado River	" "
	MAY. s. Sh.	J. B. Slaughter	Crosby Co. Tex.	Dockums Ranch "
	M X	G. M. Casey		Clinton Mo.
	M. V.	J. N. Simpson	Baylor " "	Dallas Texas
	MOB. ls. Bh.	M. T. Ikard	Clay " "	Henrietta "
	MH. bh.			
	M. s. Bh.	G. M. Casey	{ See Characters for particulars }	Clinton Mo
	M. hip.			
	MW s Bth.	E. C. Sugg & Bro	J. T.	Gainesville Texas
	MW side.			
	MYW s Yth.	Glasgow Cattle & Co	Young Co	Graham "
	MAS			
	MOL Es. old brand under brands	J. R. Hudson	Nolan & Llano Cos	Burnett "

Ear Marks.	BRANDS.	NAME.	RANCHE.	POST OFFICE.
⊙⊙	MT	J. J. Hittson Millsap & Milliken	Dbl Mt Fork	Weatherford Colorado Texas
⊙⊙	M.E.S ⊦ n	J. H. Stone & Bro		Henrietta "
⊙⊙	MBA Cs	J. B. Wilson	Concho Co.	Dallas "
⊙⊙	MILT Ls. J. 73	Franklin L & C. Co.	Greer "	Toms "
⊙⊙	M 4	Lexington	Garza Co	Fort Worth "
∞⊙	MT4	Cat Co.		
∞				
∞				
∞				
∞				
∞				
∞				
∞				
∞				
∞				

51

Ear Marks.	BRANDS.	NAME.	RANCHE.	POST OFFICE.
	NET. side 7 hip	Curtis & Atkinson Moore & West	King & Knox Co's Texas	Henrietta Jacksboro Texas
	NET. side	" "	" " "	" " "
	N XX N cs	J. W. York	Garza " "	Fort Worth "
	N B	Alamo Cattle Co	Clear fork Brazos	" " "
	N. Z. N.	Clay M. Mann	Kent & Borden cos Tex	Colorado City "
	NE X. side 9	" " "	" " " "	" " "
	N side th			
	NLY. "	Espuela Cattle Co	N. W. Texas	Fort Worth "
	NK "			
Horse	N	Joseph Campbell	Clay Co Texas	Henrietta "
	NUG. ls oth.			
	NUG. ls oth.	J. C. Loving	Jack & Young co's "	Jacksboro
Horse	NUG. lh oth.	For particulars.	See brands under M heading.	
	NN left side	H. A. Pierce	Howard Co Tex	Waxahatchie " "
	N	A. P. Bush jr	Scurry " "	Colorado City " "
	NEW.	Sam Lazarus	King & Dicken " "	for Sherman Seymour "

Ear Marks.	BRANDS.	NAME.	RANCHE.	POST OFFICE.
OO	NOX			
OO	— NOX	James W Knox	Juck M. Texa	Jacksboro Texas
OO	NOX Side 'I			
OO	N. Cor J.	J. W. Corn	Turrant " "	Bear Creek "
OO	N. Cor Sh. Some cattle sold in 1883 to G. M.	Miller + Now held in 1317.	15 mile south of Caldwell. Ks.
OO	N.	Morris + Brown		Gainesville Texas
OO	NB. hip.	G. M. Casey	{See Characters	Clinton Mo
OO	NOL. Side	" "	for particulars}	" " "
OO	NEW Ls. D.B. Gardner		Dickens + Kings Co.	Albany Texas
OM	NN	Mataser Land Ba	Motley Co.	Fort Worth "
OM	NN s. N2	Cattle Co.		
OO				
OO				
OO				
OO				
OO				

53

Ear Marks.	BRANDS.	NAME.	RANCHE.	POST OFFICE.
⊗⊗	OD.es. 25 or MC hip.	Red River Cattle Co	Clay. Co. Texas	Gainesville Texas
⊗⊗	00. Side. Oth.			
⊗⊗	00 "	Hopson & Reynolds	Cherokee N[?] BIT " "	
⊗⊗	O:Sth.	Some she Cattle in last	brand sold to F. R. Sherwood & now held in Pan handle	
⊗⊗	Obs. 73f.			
Rℬ	Obs. Sometime 73f.	W. S. Ikard	Archer. Co. Texas.	Henrietta Texas
Horses ⊗⊗	Olhorth Sometime 73h.			
⊗⊗	OTo. Vh. s.	Kimberlin Cattle Co	Greer " & BIT	Sherman "
⊗⊗	oTo. V.	" " "	" " "	" "
⊗⊗	O2:Sth.	T. S. Wade	Clay. Co. Tex.	Whitesboro "
⊗⊗	QO	E. L. Morris	Mud Creek Bit	Spanish Fort "
⊗O	ONO. side			
⊗⊗	ONO. "			
⊗⊗	Osh. ⊟ side	C. G. Graham	Montague. Co. Tex.	Gainesville "
⊗O	O.. BoBs.			
⊗O	O s & hip bone			

54

Ear Marks.	BRANDS.	NAME.	●	RANCHE.	POST OFFICE.
⊕⊕	O. left side	D. S. Donald		Denton Co. Texas	Lewisville Texas
⊕⊕	Φ.m. Φ.s. Φ.hip.				
⊘⊘	Φ.m. Φ.s. Φ.h.	Everhart & Ember		Greer " "	Doans Store " "
⊘⊘	Φ.m. Φ.s. Φ.h.				
⊕⊕	O+F. l.s.	J. W. Harding		"	Baird City " "
⊘⊘	O+F. l.s.				
⊕⊕	O+P. l.s.	W. W. Tuttle		Stonewall " "	Fort Worth " "
⊘⊘	OX. r.h & s.				
⊕⊕	OX. r.h.s. 76.n.	Forsythe Land & Cattle Co		Cottle " "	Gainesville " "
⊕⊕	OX. r.h & s. O.h.	there was sold in 1883 out of these		+ other brands belonging to this Company. 2500 head of
⊘⊘	O—O. l.s. O.h.	1-2 & 3 year old steers to		Smith & Forsythe, now held on Canadian 180 +
⊘⊘	OLO side	Espuela Cattle Co		N. W. Texas	Fort Worth, Texas
⊕⊕	O Z E E from spine to flank	C. F. Acers		Clay Co Texas	Henrietta "
⊕⊕	E E. s.	" "		" " "	" " "
⊕⊕	OV all steers	Barefoot & Bryant		Wichita " "	Montague "
Horses ⊕⊕	OV	" "		" " "	" " "

55

Ear Marks.	BRANDS.	NAME.	RANCHE.	POST OFFICE.
⟨⟩ ⟨⟩	O→▷ s. n.			
⟨⟩ ⟨⟩	O→▷ s. n. }	E. C. Sugg & Bro	Beaver Creek B1T	Gainesville Texas
⟨⟩ ⟨⟩	OK side }			
⟨⟩ ⟨⟩	OUL }	Louisville L. & Cattle Co	King Co Texas	Seymour "
⟨⟩ ⟨⟩	OU2 }	" " "	" " " "	" "
⟨⟩ ⟨⟩	OL. rs or s. rth	J. C Loving	Jack & Young "	Jacksboro "
⟨⟩ ⟨⟩	OWL. ℓ.s. }	For particulars	See brands under M heading	
⟨⟩ ⟨⟩	OWL. ℓ.s. O n }			
⟨⟩ ⟨⟩	OKS. ℓs.	G. D. Oaks	Palo Pinto Co Tex	Mineral Wells "
⟨⟩ ⟨⟩	OCT rs. T. Lyndsey Bedford & Hinton	J. C. Lindsey	Jack " "	Benjamin Tex
⟨⟩ ⟨⟩	OCT ss. T.	Some cattle sold to	B. R. Cott & Co. rebranded ◁ or ⋈	Jacksboro "
⟨⟩ ⟨⟩	O o ooo O s. n.	also some to	Harness Bros " " O 2 O.	
⟨⟩ ⟨⟩	O. HEL }	Z. T. Addington	B I T	Gainesville Texas
⟨⟩ ⟨⟩	O rn. ↑ s. O h. }	" "	"	" "
⟨⟩ ⟨⟩	O→O. bs. }	J. H. McKenzie	Andrews Co Tex	Colorado City "
⟨v⟩ ⟨m⟩	φ	" "	" " "	" " "

56

Ear Marks	Brands	Name	Ranche	Post Office
		Wilson & Morris		
	O|O left side	J. H. Wilson & Bro	Montague Co Tex	Spanish Fort Texas
	O.lsh. 98's	W. H. Williams	B1T	Erin Spring B1T
Horse	O.lth. Q.	A. P. Bush Jr	Scurry Co Tex	Colorado City Tex
	O-O.side St.	Gainesville L. & Cattle Co	Hardeman " "	Gainesville " "
	ONTST.m Jr.	James H. Knox	Jack Co Tex	Jacksboro " "
	O.Either S.	Arlington Cattle Co	Nolan " "	Burnett "
	OLD	Matador " "	Ballard Spring	Fort Worth "
	O.s	W. B. Worsham	Hardeman Co Tex	Henrietta "
	OOO.rs O.hip		" " "	Sherman " "
	OTO.y	A. S. Belcher	Clay " "	Gainesville "
	OSO.	" "	" " "	" " "
	O.shoulder	S. T. Reynolds	Young " "	Roanoke "
	O. " 2.h	" "	" " "	" " "
		J. W. Wilson	Concho " "	Gainesville "

57

Ear Marks.	BRANDS.	NAME.	RANCHE.	POST OFFICE.
	O S. side			
	O S. " C. f.	C. C. Slaughter	Colorado River	Dallas Texas
	O sh. HOP. s.			
	O. COD			
	O f. ⏝ h.			
	O.	G. M. Casey	{See Characters	Clinton Mo.
	OH. hip		for particulars}	
	OX. b. 53 Ed. A East	A. R. Witton	Archer Co Texas	Archer City Texas
	£. b. OO. rs	A. L. Butler	Clay " "	Henrietta "
	O side hip Void	Gainesville Land & Cattle Co	Hardeman " "	Gainesville "
	O side or hip	For particulars	see Figure brands.	
	O.	Geo. E. Ball	Cooke Co Texas	Gainesville "
	Oh. hip			
	O IL. side	G. M. Casey	{See Characters	Clinton Mo
	O. hip.		for particulars}	
	⊕ "			

58

Ear Marks.	BRANDS.	NAME.	RANCHE.	POST OFFICE.
	OBls. acres 60 neck	J. G. P. Boyd	Mitchell Co.	Granarien Texas
Horses OB ls.				
Ols. Sth	B. R. Cobb	Clay Co	Henrietta	"
O " Csth				
♀ ls.	G. W. Williams	Pecos River	Dallas	"
OE ls	J. B. Wilson			
O—L 75	Glasgow Causey & Co	Young Co.	Graham	"
Olsh. o.h. sy.				
Oashhog	Franklin	Greer Co.	Houns	"
Olj. A sht	Lt C Co.			
Olj. X sh Mr				
Pls. Ssht	B. R. Cobb	Clay Co.	Henrietta	"
O ls Th	J. C. Washington	I. T.	Gainsville	"
OL ls				
OX O.36j	L. M. Huntley	I. T.	Perr I. T.	
Oea. hsth	W. S. I Kund	Archer Co.	Henrietta Texas

59

Ear Marks.	BRANDS.	NAME.	RANCHE.	POST-OFFICE.
	O each hip, N ribs etc	C. C. Slaughter	Running Water	Dallas Texas
	OK r.s. Kh.			
	OK r.s.	W. S. Power	Fisher Co.	Sweetwater Texas
	O l.s. Hh.			
	O2	M. F. Ikard	Clay "	Henrietta "
	O-D s. Kn			
	OK			
	OK	E. C. Sugg & Bro.	I. T.	Gainsville "
	O			
	L L			
	O I O	J. R. Hudson	Nolan & Llano Cos	Burnett "
	O O r.s.	A. L. Butler	Clay Co.	Henrietta "
	OKID l.s.	St Louis Cas Co	Lubbock Yarga and Crosby Co	No 22 Gay Bldg
	O O l.s. & Sh	Chas Schreading		St Louis Mo
	O, S l.s. O l.h.	Lexington Cas Co	Garza County	Fort Worth Tex
	OJ O s O h			
	O l.h. S h.p. S s. l.cows	Mullin Cattle Co Mi Ikard	Oak River Archer Co	Colorado City " Henrietta (Back of book)

60

Ear Marks.	BRANDS.	NAME.	RANCHE.	POST OFFICE.
	PS. lh & s. }	Childress & Hennell Bros	Clear fork Brazos	Eliasville. Young Co. Texas
	PS. rh & s. }	" " "	" " "	" " "
	PID.s. ♡ h. 60 n.	L. Hearne		Belle Plain "
	PAN }	Catlett & Malin	Head Colorado River	Colorado City "
	PAN }	" "	" " "	" " "
	PAT. ls. Hth. void	A. L. Henson	Jack Co Texas	Jacksboro "
	PUT	M. Ikard	Archer " "	Henrietta "
	P̄	Adams & Holloway	Borden " "	Colorado City "
	POS	Louisville L & Cattle Co.	King " "	Seymour "
	POP	M. O. Lynn	Stonewall " "	Palo Pinto "
	Ꝑ	J. W. McComb	Jack " "	Jacksboro "
	POOR	H. M. void Childress	Knox " "	Seymour "
	P8. side nick	Gainesville L & Cattle Co	Hardeman " "	Gainesville "
	PIG	W. E. Rayner	Knox " "	Seymour "
	Ꝓ	Matador Cattle Co	Ballard Springs	Fort Worth "
	PEL	J. D. Reed	Camp Supply BIT	" " "

61

Ear Marks.	BRANDS.	NAME.	RANCHE.	POST OFFICE.
	P R.	J. N. Simpson	Baylor Co Tex	Dallas Texas
	P H. es. u.	W. B. Worsham	Hardeman " "	Henrietta "
	PAT }	Curtis & Atkinson	Panhandle " "	" "
	PET J	" " "	" " "	" " "
	POT	S. F. Reynolds	Jack Co. "	Roanoke "
	PF. P. sis.	J. W. Wilson	Concho " "	Gainesville "
	P. sh. s ship.	Mabry, Glasgow & Crawford	Cottle " "	Graham "
	POG. es. OO. rs.	J. L. Butler	Clay " " Henrietta "
	PC. es. OO. rs }	(Some times with =	out the O.O. in rs.)
	ю. s. P. h. }		" " "	" "
	PL. hip }	G. M. Casey	(See Character	Clinton Mo
	ꝗ hip }		for particulars
	ꝗ hip }		
	PEL es. Dawson	Void Ward & Byer	See J & brand for particulars —
	PUT	A. Putnam Jr.	Erath Co. Stephenville Texas
	PA☐ es.	Wm. S. Power	Fisher Co. Sweetwater "

62

Ear Marks.	BRANDS.	NAME.	RANCHE.	POST OFFICE.
⊂⊃	PC KsTn	Mallett Cattle C	Col River	Colorado City, Tex
∞				
∞				
∞				
∞				
∞				
∞				
∞				
⊂∞	Q QBlsNh	The Moyne Land & Cattle Co	Croton Cr King County	Seymour Tex
∞				
∞				
∞				
∞				
∞				
∞				

63

Ear Marks.	BRANDS.	NAME.	RANCHE.	POST OFFICE.
⊃⊂	RAY. Ls. ^ n.	Red River Cattle Co	Clay Co Texas	Gainesville Texas
⊃⊂	ROS. Left s.	Kit Carter Cattle Co	Dickens & King Cos "	Seymour "
⊃⊂	RAT. " "	" " " "	" " "	" " "
⊃⊂	ROP " "			
⊃⊂	ROF " "			
⊃⊂	ROF " "	A. B. Roff.	Chickasaw Nt BIT	Gainesville "
⊃⊂	R R " "			
⊃⊂	F " "			
⊃⊂	F " "			
⊃⊂	ROP. side	Espuela Cattle co	N. W. Texas	Fort Worth "
⊃⊂	ROX "	" "	" " "	" " "
⊃⊂	R Ls & hip.	C. F. Acers	Clay. Co. Tex	Henrietta "
⊃⊂	R P. left side	" "	" " "	" "
Horses ⊃⊂	Ⓡ	Joseph Campbell	" " "	" "
Horses ⊃⊂	R. l hip.	C. C. Rumrill	Knox " "	Gainesville "
⊃⊂	RUSL. Ls.	J. L. Hull	Clay " "	Secret Spring "

64

Ear Marks.	BRANDS.	NAME.	RANCHE.	POST OFFICE.
⊗⊘	R T			
⊗⊘	RIDR	Louisville Land & Cattle Co.	King Co Tex	Seymour Texas
⊘	RIDR			
⊗⊘	RUS. l.s.	G. D. Oaks	Palo Pinto " "	Mineral Wells "
⊗⊘	RUS. l.s. J.th.	" " "	" " " "	" " "
⊘	R. corb s.	J. M. McKenzie	Andrews " "	Colorado City "
⊘	RV. left s.	" " "	" " " "	" " "
⊗	ЯP	Matador Cattle Co	Ballard Spring "	Fort Worth "
⊗	ROSS.	J. N. Simpson	Baylor Co Tex	Dallas "
⊗⊘	Я 2. is.	W. B. Worsham	Hardeman " "	Henrietta "
⊗⊘	R—S	J. D. Reed	Camp Supply R I T	Fort Worth "
⊗⊘	R. N	" "	" " "	" " "
⊗⊘	ROH	G. M. Casey	See Character	Clinton Mo.
⊗⊘	RED is.	M. F. Skard	Clay Co Tex	Henrietta Tex
⊗⊘	RE. both	" "	" " "	" " "
⊗⊘	R3 hip	G. M. Casey	See Character	Clinton Mo

65

Ear Marks.	BRANDS.	NAME.	RANCHE.	POST OFFICE.
⊗⊙	ROK }	J. R. Hudson	Nolan & Llano Cos	Burnett Texas
⊗⊙	RFT }			
∞	RP l.s.	W. B. Gardner	Dickens & King Cos.	Albany "
⊗⊙	ROY. H. Willsap & Milliken		L.G. Mtr. Fork	Weatherford Tx " Colorado "
⊗⊙	RTC l.s.	W. S. Power	Fisher Co.	Sweetwater "
⊗⊙	RB RB	E. C. Sugg & Bro	I. T.	Gainsville "
⊗⊙	R+ l.s. { St Louis Car Co		Lubbock Garza	No 22 Gay Bldng
⊗⊙	ROS l.s. Chas Schunding &c, &c		new brosby	St Louis Mo
⊗⊙	ROD Lexington Car Co		Garza Co	Fort Worth Tx
∞				
∞				
∞				
∞				
∞				
∞				
∞				

66

Ear Marks.	BRANDS.	NAME.	RANCHE.	POST OFFICE.
⊙⊙	SUB. ls. sh. SU	Red River Cattle Co	Clay Co Tex	Gainesville Texas
⊙⊙	SU. ls. S h.	" " "	" " "	" "
⊙⊙	SP. rn. co.	L. Hearne		Belle Plain "
⊙⊙	SUL. ls.	Kit Carter Cattle Co	Dickens & King " "	Seymour "
⊙⊙	SPC. s.	" " " "	" " " " "	" "
⊙⊙	S. ls & th	E. P. Swenson	Jones " "	New York City "
⊘◍	S. is & th	" " "	" " " " "	" "
⊘◍	SET. c.			
⊙⊗	SET. ls. E.	Ewen, Small & Stinson	Palo Pinto " "	Palo Pinto (box 34) "
⊙◔	SNEL. ls.			
⊙⊙	SN. ls. BS. h.			
⊘⊙	S. sh. Sc. sid. S. sh. Co.	G. Graham	Montague " "	Gainesville "
⊘◒	SD. thro.	D. S. Donald	Denton " "	Lewisville "
⊙⊘	SG. thro.	H. H. McConnell	Jack " "	Jacksboro "
⊙⊙	ST. hirny place	A L. Stinson	" " "	" " "
⊙⊙	SAM. rn. SAM.	J. C. Carpenter	Wise " "	Decatur "

Ear Marks.	BRANDS.	NAME.	RANCHE.	POST OFFICE.
	CS ▷	Clay M. Mann	Kent & Borden Co's Tex	Colorado City Texas
	L. cs. T. cong	W. W. Tuttle	Stonewall " "	Fort Worth "
	SOR side.	Espuela Cattle Co	N. W. Texas	" " "
	SAE "	" " " "	" " " "	" " "
	SE	Glidden & Sanborn	Potter & Randall co's Tex	Houston "
	SAB } these brands bought of Acar		or Witherspoon (see Characters)	
	SOX			
Horses	SH } Joseph Campbell		Clay Co. Tex.	Henrietta "
Horses	SL	" " "	" " " " " "	
	S	Louisville Land & Cattle Co	King " "	Seymour " "
	S2 John H Belcher & Belcher		Montague " "	Gainesville " "
	Sy (S l or chip)			
	(S) l chip } J. L. Hull		Clay " "	Secret Springs " "
	(S) l or chip			
	SR Dan Waggoner & Son		North Texas & B.I.T	Decatur " "
	S S B. H. Dennis		Hood & Stephens co Tex	Granbury " "

68

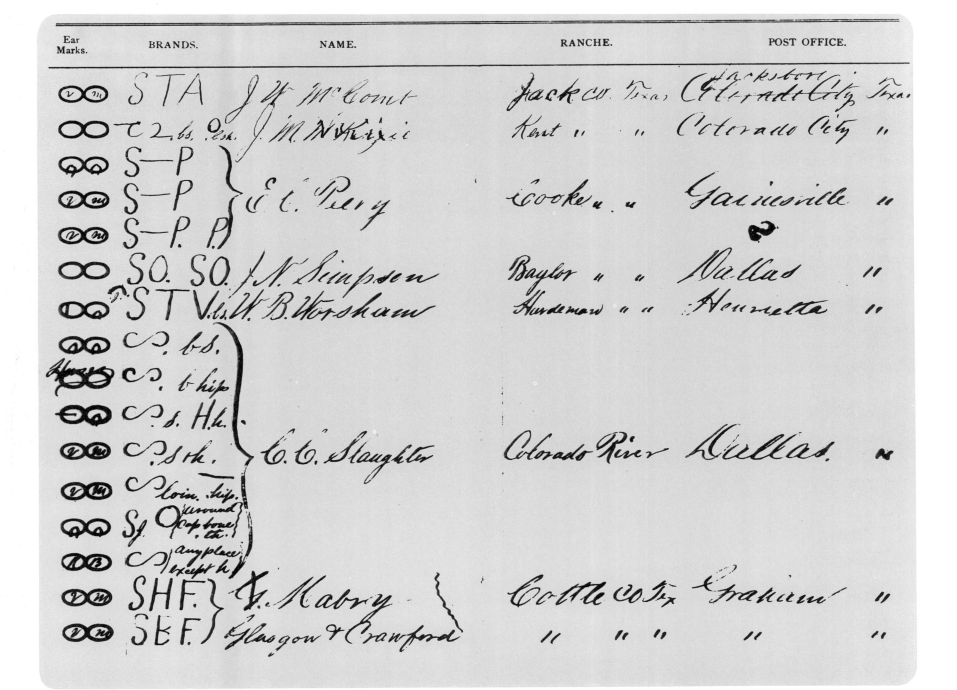

Ear Marks.	BRANDS.	NAME.	RANCHE.	POST OFFICE.
⬭⬭	STA	J. W. McCount	Jack Co. Texas	Jacksboro Colorado City Texas
⬭⬭	C 2. bs. Oesh.	J. M. McKinzie	Kent " "	Colorado City "
⬭⬭	S—P	}	Cooke " "	Gainesville "
⬭⬭	S—P	} E. C. Perry		
⬭⬭	S—P. P.	}		
⬭⬭	SO. SO.	J. N. Simpson	Baylor " "	Dallas "
⬭⬭	STV. bs.	W. B. Worsham	Hardeman " "	Henrietta "
⬭⬭	CP. bs.			
⬭⬭	CP. b. hips			
⬭⬭	CP. b. H.h.			
⬭⬭	CP. S. h. }	C. C. Slaughter	Colorado River	Dallas "
⬭⬭	CP loin. hip.			
⬭⬭	Sh O around hip bone. th.			
⬭⬭	CP any place except h.			
⬭⬭	SHF. }	J. Mabry	Cottle Co. Tex	Graham "
⬭⬭	SBF. }	Glasgow & Crawford	" " "	" "

69

Ear Marks.	BRANDS.	NAME.	RANCHE.	POST OFFICE.
	S/L.	E. M. Casey	{See Characters for particulars}	Clinton Mo
	S/X.	" "		" " "
	S left sh.	J. N. Simpson	Baylor Co Tex	Dallas Texas
	S r.sh.+ th.	Cline & Sparks	I. T.	Gainesville "
	S left sh. & j.			
	SRE	J. J. Hicmson	W.H. Mt. Fork	Weatherford Tex "
	SAP. Rh.	Wallcape & Milliken		Colorado "
	SEr			
	SAN	Curtis & Atkinson	Panhandle	Henrietta Texas
	S∽S			
	SMEs. h Dawson Ward & Byler		Pecos River	Fort Worth Texas
	S∽2Ls. Chas Corn		Palo Pinto Co.	Weatherford "
	S r.sh. + th. J. H. Wire & Bro			Henrietta "
	S∽S Red River Cattle Co.		Clay Co.	Gainesville "
	SUELs. 73. Franklin L. & C Co.		Greer Co.	Doans
	SH Mrs. W. T. Power		Fisher Co.	Sweetwater "

70

Ear Marks.	BRANDS.	NAME.	RANCHE.	POST OFFICE.
⊙⊙	S+P	Baum & Collins	Knox Co.	Henrietta Texas
⊙⊙	STB			
⊙⊙	ST ls. th.	J. C. Washington	I. T.	Gainesville "
⊙⊙	T rs. th.			
⊙⊙	S 31 ls.			
⊙⊙	S 3 l.s. rf.	C. M. Tilford	Crosby Co.	Colorado "
⊙∞	S 32 ls.			
⊙⊙	ssrl Sh.	Tornado Express	Wheis Greer Co.	Doan Graham Tex. "
∞	SK sLs. L 53 rs.	J. S. Legan		
∞				
∞				
∞				
∞				
∞				
∞				

71

Ear Marks.	BRANDS.	NAME.	RANCHE.	POST OFFICE.
	⅂ rs.	Hopson & Reynolds	Cherokee Nt BIT	Gainesville Texas
	TXL s.in.	W. S. Ikard	Archer Co Tex	Henrietta "
	F (on 4 year old & over) (arm le brand)	Kimberlin Cattle Co	Greer " & BIT	Sherman "
	T. ⌒O⌒.		" "	Henrietta "
	JO. Sth.	Curtis & "Atkinson" Moore & West	King & Knox Cos Tex	Jacksboro "
	F in. ☐ s. Ftn.	Wilson & Morris E. L. Morris	Mud Creek BIT	Spanish Fort "
	T. left side.	S. B. Burnett	Wichita. Co. Tex.	Fort Worth "
	₸. " "	A. B. Roff	Chickasaw Nt. BIT	Gainesville "
	T.rs. #L S.hip.	Adams Cattle Co	Clear fork Brazos	Fort Worth "
	TP.L.2 TP.h.	" "	" " "	" " "
	T.s. T side.	D. T. Phillips	Hall Co Texas	Valley View "
	T.nrsh. P side.	T. H. Burnett	Archer " "	Henrietta "
	TOP.e side.	J. A. Wilson	Greer " "	Vernon "
	TOP. e side.		" " "	Fort Worth "
	T.sj TH.2	W. W. Tuttle	Stonewall " "	Fort Worth "
	T.ej. sh & hip.	" "	" " "	" " "

72

Ear Marks.	BRANDS.	NAME.	RANCHE.	POST OFFICE.
	T Z ös.			
	" "			
	" "B'k"			
	" "R"	L. E. Ikard	Archer. Co. Tex	Henrietta Texas
	" "U"			
	" "M"			
	" "F"			
	" "L"			
	" "T"			
	Tsh V s.	Adams & Holloway	Borden " "	Colorado City "
	V left side.	Forsythe L. & Cattle Co	Cottle " "	Gainesville "
	J side & hip.	Espuela Cattle "	N. W. Texas	Fort Worth "
	FO side.	" " "	" "	" " "
	T O / O / T	Barefoot & Bryant.	Chickasaw Nation	Montague "

73

Ear Marks.	BRANDS.	NAME.	RANCHE.	POST OFFICE.
⊘⊙	Tex. s. u. &f. }	H. Y. Bedford	Knox Co Texas	Seymour Tex
⊘⊘	TX ls.u. S }	" "	" " "	" " "
Horses ⊘⊘	T. th. north	A. B. Roff	Chickasaw Nt Bit	Gainesville "
Horses ⊘⊘	Tex. W th.	Geo A. Cooke	Stephen Co Tex	Strawn "
⊘⊘	TOAD }			
⊘⊘	TOB }	Louisville Lt Cattle Co.	King " "	Seymour "
⊘⊘	TRA }			
⊘⊘	Trs.	J. L. Hull	Clay " "	Secret Springs "
⊘⊘	TIM.ls.	Chas E. Brown	Young " "	Belknap "
⊘⊘	TOBY.ls.	B. H. Dennis	Hood & Stephen " "	Granbury "
⊘⊙	T	John H. Stone	N. W. Texas	Gainesville "
⊘⊘	TT	H. A. Pierce	Howard co Tex	Waxahatchie "
⊘⊘	Lou	F. T. Addington	B I T	Gainesville "
⊘⊘	TEL.ls. }	Wm Harris		
Horses ⊘⊘	TEL " }	W. Scott.	Colorado & Pecos Riv	Colorado City "
		"	" " "	" " "
⊘⊘	TBt.ls.	A. P. Bush Jr	Scurry Co. Tex	" " "

74

Ear Marks.	BRANDS.	NAME.	RANCHE.	POST OFFICE.
⊙⊙	TIB. side.	J. W. Hutchinson	Throckmorton Co Tex	Decatur Texas
⊙⊙	TIB. s. h.	" " "	" " "	" " "
⊙⊙	TOP. hors.	H. F. Moore	Kaufman " "	Kaufman "
⊙⊙	TOP. hors.	" "	" " "	" " "
⊙⊙	TED. Es.	Arlington Cattle Co	Nolan " "	Burnett "
⊙⊙	T. both side			
⊙⊙	T. side or back	Matador " "	Ballard Spring	Fort Worth "
⊙⊙	TIL			
⊙⊙	T41			
⊙⊙	F. O.	A. S. Belcher	Clay Co Texas	Gainesville "
⊙⊙	F. O.	Kimberlin Cat. Co	" " " "	Sherman Tex
⊙⊙	H hip			
⊙⊙	Y. s. th.			
⊙⊙	T. hip	C. C. Slaughter	Colorado River	Dallas "
⊙⊙	H. side			
⊙⊙	o I I			

75

Ear Marks.	BRANDS.	NAME.	RANCHE.	POST OFFICE.
⌾ ⌾	T. sh. 8.th.	Mabry, Glasgow & Crawford	Cottle Co. Tex.	Graham, Texas.
○○	TCA	G. M. Casey.	See Character	Clinton Mo.
○○	ᴎ Void	J. L. Reed		
○○	TRA. ih.	J. H. Stradley	Jack " "	Jacksboro Texas
○○	TM. is. 53 in. Ed A. Cash	R. H. Milton	Archer " "	Archer City "
○○	VAB.	Sam Lazarus	King & Dicken " "	for skinman Seymour "
○○	F. l side. O hip.	W H Williams	BIT.	Erin Springs BIT.
○○	F. l sor h.	" "	"	" " "
○○	TT. Side	G. M. Casey	{ For particulars	Clinton Mo
⌾ ⌾	TOY.	" "	See Character	" "
⌾ ⌾	TAY.	" "	brands	" "
○○	TIL. l.s. h. th.	B. R. Cobb	Clay Co.	Henrietta Texas
○○	TIL. " L "			"
○○	J & R.B. Void	Hansin Ward & a Byers	Pecos River	Fort Worth "
○○	Tech X h	Hitson		
⌾ ⌾	TID	Millsape & Milliken	Lbl & Mt. Fork	Weatherford Colorado "

76

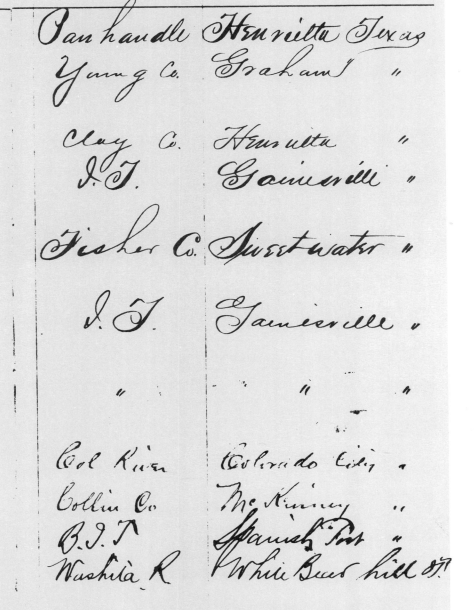

Ear Marks.	BRANDS.	NAME.	RANCHE.	POST OFFICE.
∞	TOM	Curtis & Atkinson	Pan handle	Henrietta Texas
∞	T+ Tho. Pth	Glasgow Causey & Co.	Young Co.	Graham "
∞	" E.S. "			
∞	T4 E.s.oh	J H Stine & Bro	Clay Co.	Henrietta "
∞	TOM l.s.	J. C. Washington	I.T.	Gainesville "
∞	T+ ls			
∞	TR O l.s.	W S Power	Fisher Co.	Sweet water "
∞	TOM			
∞	TX	L. T. Arrington	I.T.	Gainesville "
∞	+ Tx [under tail]			
∞	T 75 (all over)	E. C. Sugg & Bro	"	" "
∞	TG P side	Mallett Cat Co	Col River	Colorado City "
∞	"" JIM opposite			
∞	T l.s I s Ship	J. M. Hill	Collin Co	McKinney "
∞	Ⱦ E.s.	W. H. Yarbrough	B.I.T	Spanish Post "
∞	T hip 7 ughr horn sawer 77	G. J. Garvin	Washita R	White Bear hill I T

77

Ear Marks.	BRANDS.	NAME.	RANCHE.	POST OFFICE.
∞	U Sth. Jaw X	Curtis & Atkinson Moore & West	King & Knox Cos Tex.	Henrietta & Jacksboro Texas
∞	U 7 Z	M. Shard	Archer " "	Henrietta "
∞	U L Λ ⟩	Glidden & Sanborn	Potter & Randall " "	Houston "
∞	U L ⟩	For Particular	See Character Brands.	
∞	U Ls. Sth. ⟩	W. B. Slaughter	Crosby. Co. Tex.	Dockums Ranch "
⊘⊘	U C⌐ Usor loin		" " "	" " "
∞	U U. Either Side.	C. W. Word	North Texas & I.T.	Kansas City, Mo.
∞	U Lth or loin. ⟩	D. W. Burnett	Tom Green Co Tex	Dallas Texas
∞	U L hip. Jaw		" " "	" "
∞	U̲ Either Side.	Geo Harris	Colorado & Pecos River	Colorado City "
∞	U	J. D. Reed	Baylor Co Tex	Fort Worth "
∞	U P	J. N. Simpson	Baylor Co Tex	Dallas "
∞	U C⌐ ⟩	J. B. Slaughter	Crosby " "	Dockums Ranche "
∞	∩ C⌐ ⟩	" " "	" " "	" "
∞	⌂ U⌐ side	G. M. Casey	See Character	Clinton Mo
∞ Horns	U L hip	Jim Montgomery	Kent Co.	Fort Worth Texas

Ear Marks.	BRANDS.	NAME.	RANCHE.	POST OFFICE.
∞	UTΛ }	Curtis & d	Panhandle	Henrietta Texas
∞	UΛ }	Atkinson		
∞	UX ls }	J. N. Groesbeck	Erath Co.	Stephenville "
∞	UX " }			
∞	U1 s L.	W. B. Slaughter	Crosby Co.	
∞	UHID ls.	St Louis Car Co.	Lubbock Co. C	22 Fay Bldng St Louis Mo
∞	U ls.	"	"	"
∞				
∞				
∞				
∞				
∞				
∞				
∞				
∞				

Ear Marks.	BRANDS.	NAME.	RANCHE.	POST OFFICE.
⊘ ⊘	V y/aw. K behind shoulder			
⊘ ⊘	V sh. K s. Λ th	Kimberlin Cattle Co	Greer Co Tex + BIT	Sherman Texas
⊘ ⊘	V sh. Λ (a/all steers)			
⊟ ⊟	V hip.			
⊟ ⊟	V side H hip.	Espuela Cattle Co	N. W. Texas	Fort Worth "
⊟ ⊟	V side S hip.			
⊘ ⊘	V es. R.B. side	C. F. Acers	Clay Co Texas	Henrietta "
Horses ⊘⊘	V left Sh.			
Horses ⊘⊘	V esh. 73 sc.	W. S. Ikard	Archer " "	" " "
Horses ⊘⊘	V eth or hip.			
⊘ ⊘	VD.	A P. Bush Jr	Scurry " "	Colorado City "
⊘ ⊘	V V		" " "	" " "
⊘ ⊘	V Side & hip.	Gainesville L & Cattle Co		Gainesville "
⊘ ⊘	V " "			
⊟ ⊟	—V	James W. Knox	Jack " "	Jacksboro "
⊘ ⊘	VAIL	J. N. Simpson	Baylor " "	Dallas "

80

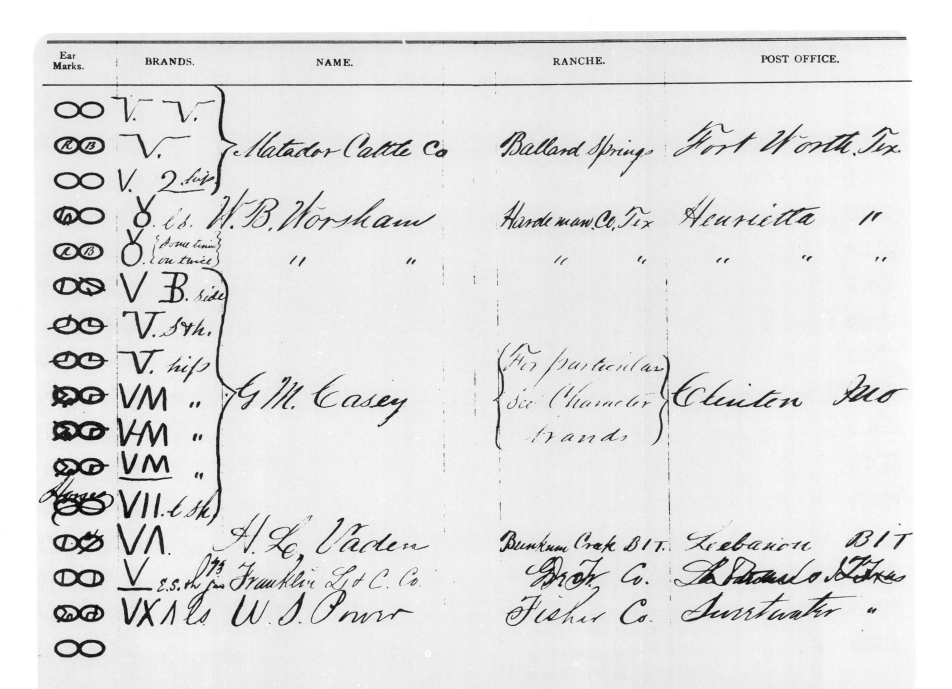

Ear Marks.	BRANDS.	NAME.	RANCHE.	POST OFFICE.
∞	V. V.			
∞	V.	Matador Cattle Co	Ballard Springs	Fort Worth. Tex.
∞	V. 2 hip.			
∞	♂ es.	W. B. Worsham	Hardeman Co. Tex	Henrietta "
∞	♂ {Some times on twice}	" "	" "	" " " "
∞	V B. side			
∞	V. S th.			
∞	V. hip		{For particular see Character brands}	Clinton Mo
∞	VM "	G M Casey		
∞	VM "			
∞	VM "			
∞	VII. l. sh.			
∞	VΛ.	A. L. Vaden	Bunkum Creek B.I.T.	Lebanon B.I.T
∞	V E.S. th. jaw Franklin L. & C. Co.		Bro. Co.	
∞	VXΛ es. W. S. Porr		Fisher Co.	Sweetwater "
∞				

81

Ear Marks.	BRANDS.	NAME.		RANCHE.	POST OFFICE.
	WD. left S.	Red River Cattle Co		Clay Co Texas	Gainesville Texas
	W M. es.	" " " "		" " "	" " "
	WHY	Hopson & Reynolds		Cherokee Nt. Bit	" " "
	WC. es. x	W. S. Ikard		Archer. Co. Tex	Henrietta "
	WC	" "		" " "	" " "
	WO. esh.	T. S. Wade		Clay " "	Whitesboro "
	WTS. s. x	Harmonson & Cox		Young " "	Belknap "
	W. both sides	Geo. H. Goddard		Tom Green " "	St. Louis Mo
	W. both sh.	" " " "		" " " "	" " "
	WTW. es.	Kit Carter Cattle Co		Dickens & King " "	Seymour Texas
	WM. es.	" " " "		" " " "	" " "
	WP. Es	A. B. Roff		Chickasaw Nt Bit	Gainesville "
	WP. Es	" "		" " "	" " "
	WLA. es. A	Everhart & Embrer		Greer Co Texas	Doans Store "
	W7Z	M. Ikard		Archer " "	Henrietta "
	WM. es.	Joseph Campbell		Clay Co "	Henrietta "

82

Ear Marks.	BRANDS.	NAME.	RANCHE.	POST OFFICE.
	W. es. Ship.	Forsythe Land & Cattle Co	Cattle Co Texas	Gainesville Texas
	WH. Side	Espuela Cattle Co	N. W. Texas	Fort Worth " "
	WCJ "	" " "	" " "	" " " "
	WIL. es. Ship.	W. B. Slaughter	Crosby Co Texas	Lockams Ranche " "
	WIL. es. F.	" " "	" " "	" " " "
	WHY.	Louisville Land & Cattle Co	King " "	Seymour " "
	WOL. es.	G. W. Wolcott	Tom Green " "	Big Springs " "
	W. es. 5.3. nick	" "	Tom Green " "	" " " "
	W. es. E. st. & horn	James Dulin	B I T	White Bead Hill B I T
	W. es. s.	Dan Waggoner & Son	North Texas & BIT	Decatur Texas
	WT. es. Jaw			
	WT. es. W Jaw	G. W. Williams	Pecos River	Dallas " "
	WD. es.			
	WET. Void	Matthew Cartwright	Stonewall & Kaufman Co	Terrall " "
	W. es. th.	G. H. Wilson & Bro	Montague Co Tex	Spanish Fort " "
	W. es.	Wilson & Morris	" " " "	" " " "

Ear Marks.	BRANDS.	NAME.	RANCHE.	POST OFFICE.
	WT e.s. H .h.	P. C. Harmonson 1800	Archer Co Texas	Farmer, Young Co Texas
	W e.s. E .h.	A. P. Bush jr	Scurry " "	Colorado City " "
	W Either S. Gainesville L. & Cattle Co		Hardeman " "	Gainesville " "
	WK	W. E. Rayner	Knox " "	Seymour "
	WQ s.th.	J. T. Ligon	Greer " "	Graham "
	WAB. side	Grounds, Embrea " & 107 " "	" " "	Doans " "
	WH s.th.	Mabry, Glasgow & Crawford	Cottle " "	" " "
	W. hip. KM .s.	J. W. Wilson	Concho " "	Gainesville "
	WAY	G. M. Casey	See Character	Clinton Mo
	W. lsh th. I .s.	W. H. Williams	BIT.	Erin Springs BIT
	W. lsh th. H .s.	" "	"	" " "
	W lsh +.s. I .h.	" "	"	" " "
	W4. hip.	G. M. Casey.	See Character	Clinton Mo.
	WSM .s.	Cline & Hearks	I. T.	Gainesville Texas
	WES s. the	J. R. Hudson	Nolan & Llano Cos	Burnett "
	W+	Odom & Collins	Knox "	Henrietta "

84

Ear Marks.	BRANDS.	NAME.	RANCHE.	POST OFFICE.
∞	W	Curtis and	Panhandle	Henrietta Texas
∞	W	Atkinson		
∞	WIL es 73			
∞	WIL es h	Franklin Land	Greer Co.	Doans
∞	WIT es	and Cattle Co.		
∞	Wll th j	Presidio Live Stock Co	Presidio Co.	Fort Davis "
∞	WT hip	W. S. Power	Fisher "	Sweetwater "
∞	WT h.rs.			
∞	W ls Wm	R. R. Wade	North Concho.	Colorado
∞	W " W "	These are	also used as R Bs
∞	WEL Es	St Louis Car Co	Lubbock. G O	No 22 Gay Bldg St Louis
∞	WEN	G. H. Goddard		
∞				
∞				
∞				
∞				

85

Ear Marks.	BRANDS.	NAME.	RANCHE.	POST OFFICE.
	X2 ls.	C M Tilford	Crosby Co	Colorado Texas
	X21 "	Jno Harris		
	— X	W. Scott		

Ear Marks.	BRANDS.	NAME.	RANCHE.	POST OFFICE.
	XL }	W. S. Ikard	Archer Co. Texas	Henrietta Texas
	XL }	" "	" " "	" " "
	X side X etc.	D. H. Philips	Hall " "	Valley View "
	XXX }	Clay. M. Mann	Kent & Borden " "	Colorado City "
	XXX }	" "	" " " "	" " "
	X side + hip	Espuela Cattle Co	N. W. Texas	Fort Worth "
	XO es. O h. " }	E. F. Acers	Clay Co "	Henrietta "
	X1 left side	" "	" " " "	" " "
	XO 4 " " }	J. L. Hall	" " "	Scent Springs "
	X4 rh + h.	" "	" " "	" " "
	XTS	J. W. Mooar Bros	Scurry " "	Colorado City "
	X X	F. T. Waite	Pauls Valley I.T.	Pauls Valley I.T.
	XH. hip & side }	A. P. Bush jr	Scurry Co Tex	Colorado City Texas
	XH. side }	" "	" " "	" " " "
	X ss	W. B. Worsham	Hardeman " "	Henrietta "
	XS	A. S. Belcher	Clay " "	Gainesville "

87

Ear Marks.		BRANDS.	NAME.	RANCHE.	POST OFFICE.
⊙⊙		X	J. M. Fowler	Clay Co. Texas	Riverland Texas
⊙⊙		X 3.	Gainesville Land & Cattle Co.	For particulars see Figure brands	"
⊙⊙		X: 21.	Morris & Brown		Gainesville "
⊙⊙		X. hip.	G. M. Casey	For particular	Clinton Mo
⊙⊙		X. l. hip.	" " "	see Character	" "
⊙⊙		XYZ	" " "	brands	" "
⊙⊙		XL	Curtis and	Panhandle	Henrietta Texas
⊙⊙		XXL	Atkinson		
⊙⊙		X X √RB.			
⊙⊙		X —	Warren Ward	Pecos R.	Fort Worth "
⊙⊙		X — ana RB	and Tyler		
⊙⊙		X sh. sh.	Red River Cattle Co.	Clay Co.	Gainesville "
⊙⊙		X ls. & ls.	Franklin L. & C. Co.	Greer Co.	Downs "
⊙⊙		X lsh x j			
⊙⊙		XCD ls.	W S Power	Fisher Co.	Sweetwater "
⊙⊙		XCD ls. C sh.			

88

Ear Marks.	BRANDS.	NAME.	RANCHE.	POST OFFICE.
	Y+ Y (es. Yth)	J. C. Loving	Jack & Young Co. Ir.	Jacksboro Texas
	Y+ Y (es. Ya)	" "	" " " "	" " "
	Ys. YS.	M O'Lynn	Stonewall Co. Texas	Palo Pinto "
	Y.G. U side.	J. W. McComb	Jack " "	Jacksboro "
	Ys. esth. H. Scott	Jno Harris	Colorado & Pecos Rivers.	Colorado City "
	Y R	A. P. Bush jr	Scurry Co. Texas	" " "
	YAR. XX.	Mabry, Glasgow & Crawford	Cottle " "	Graham "
	YX ls.	G. W. Oakes	Palo Pinto Co.	Mineral Wells "

89

Ear Marks.	BRANDS.	NAME.	RANCHE.	POST OFFICE.
⊗⊗	ZIP.side.	Espuela Cattle Co	N. W. Texas	Fort Worth, Texas
⊘⊞	ZV left side }	C. F. Acers	Clay Co Tex	Henrietta "
⊘⊞	ZV over 8 + r.s. }	" "	" " "	" " "
⊗⊗	Z— P.scrow.	W. B. Slaughter	Crosby " "	Dockrums Ranche "
⊗⊗	SXT l.s.	J. W. Mooar Bros	Scurry " "	Colorado City "
⊗⊗	ZOZ.s. F. }	J. W. Hutchinson	Throckmorton " "	Decatur "
⊗⊗	Z/Z side. Z th. }	" " "	" " " "	" " "
⊗⊗	ZAL.	Curtis & Atkinson	Panhandle	Henrietta "
⊗⊗	ZX. }	G. M. Casey	} See character	Clinton .Mo.
⊗⊗	ZAC.side }	" "	for particulars	" "
⊘⊞	Z l.s. }	Franklin L.	Greer Co.	Doans Texas
⊘⊞	Z " }	and C. Co.		
⊗⊗	ZNZ	St Louis Cat Co	Lubbock	22 Fry Bldng St Louis
⊗⊗				
⊗⊗				
⊗⊗				

90

Ear Marks.	BRANDS.	NAME.	RANCHE.	POST OFFICE.
		Red River Cattle Co	Clay Co Texas	Gainesville Texas
		Hopson & Reynolds	Cherokee Nt. B I T	" "
		Kimberlin Cattle Co	Greer Co & B I T	Sherman
		J. P. Addington	Beaver Creek B I T	Kansas City Mo.

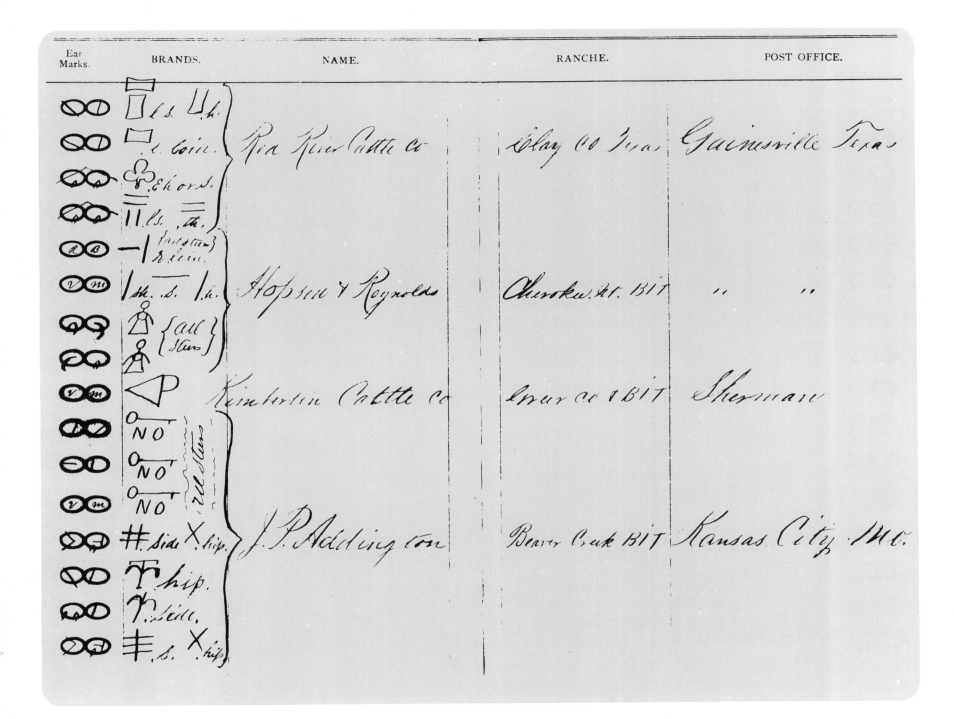

Ear Marks.	BRANDS.	NAME.	RANCHE.	POST OFFICE.
	l.sh. hip.			
	l.sh. hip.	J. S. Wade	Clay. Co Texas	Whitesboro Texas
	right hip.			
	sth. r side.	Harmonson & Cox	Young " "	Belknap " "
	⊞	E. L. Morris	Mud Creek BIT	Spanish Fort " "
	⋈ b. sides.	J. W. Zook	Garza. Co. Tex.	Fort. Worth " "
	♀	Geo. H. Goddard	Tom Green " "	St Louis Mo
	○ NO. b.s.	Kit Carter Cattle Co	Dickens & King " "	Seymour Texas
	⊥ b.s.	" " " "	" " " "	" " " "
	⊡ Side.			
	sh. \ s. \ hip			
	sh. \ s. \ hip			
	sh. R s.	C. G. Graham	Montague. Co. Tex.	Gainesville " "
	sh. R s.			
	sh. \ s.			
	sh. \ s. all stars			

92

Ear Marks.	BRANDS.	NAME.	RANCHE.	POST OFFICE.
	X .left side.	A. B. Roff	Chickasaw Nt BIT	Gainesville Texas
	—X— }	J. C. Carpenter	Wise Co Texas	Decatur "
Horses	—X·— }	" " "	" " "	" " "
	□ .ls oh. }	J. A. Wilson	Greer " "	Vernon "
	□ .ls th.	" " "	" " "	" " "
	⌂ }	Clay. M. Mann	Kent & Borden " "	Colorado City "
	⊙ three "Circle dot", Cattle are scattered from		head of San Saba River. Tex, to Powder River Ranche Wyoming.	
	△ rj. △ ls.	James Rennie	Rush Creek BIT	White Bead Hill BIT
	△ rj △ ls }	" "	" " "	" " " "
	□ s. ⊓ h. }			
	▭ .hip. }	Espuela Cattle Co	N.W. Texas	Fort Worth Texas
	▽ .side. }			
	+X . }			
	◇ ◇ }	J B Young	Clay Co Texas	Buffalo Springs "
	◇ ◇ }	" "	" " "	" " " "
	▽▽ . side.	C. F. Acer	" " "	Henrietta "

Ear Marks.	BRANDS.	NAME.	RANCHE.	POST OFFICE.
∞	⊙⎯ left side.	Gladden & Sanborn	Potter & Randall Co. Tex.	Houston Texas.
∞	Ⓐ " "	they Cast 3 with other	brands were bought of C. F. & Cos &	
∞	⎯75	J. G. & P. D. Witherspoon	Cattle in them are now running on Pease River.	
∞	⊖	in Cottle and	adjoining counties.	
∞	⋔			
⟨B⟩	+ C ℓ. side or loin			
⟨B⟩	⎡ l. Side. loin	W. B. Slaughter	Crosby. Co. Texas	Dockum's Ranche. Texas
⟨B⟩	Ø C ℓ. s. or loin			
Horse ∞	+ C ℓ. l. hip			
⟨Bar⟩	⊢▷	Barefoot & Bryant.	Chickasaw. Nt. BIT	Montague " "
⟨B⟩	⅄ (all steers) l. side.	E. C. Sugg & Bro	Beaver Creek "	Gainesville " "
Horse ∞	⅄	" " "	" " "	" " " "
⟨m⟩	+TW	Frey & Millican	Erath. Co. Texas	Stephensville " "
∞	rth. Side.	H. G. Bedford	Cottle " "	Seymour " "
⟨m⟩	⎯LO l. s.		Knox " "	" " " "
⟨m⟩	⊙	Reed Buff & Belcher John N. Belcher	Montague " "	Gainesville " "

94

Ear Marks.	BRANDS.	NAME.	RANCHE.	POST OFFICE.
⊗⊗	□□ □ es }	J. C. Loving	Jack & Young Co's	Jacksboro Texas
⊗⊗ m	□ □ ,ES, }	For particulars	see brands under M heading.	
⊗⊗	□ .g. sn. srh.	J L Hull	Clay. Co. Texas	Secret Springs "
⊗⊗ m	⊜ .bseder.	Dan Waggoner & Son	North Texas 1811	Decatur " "
⊗⊗	—	Jr. M. O'Lynn	Stonewall or Tex	Palo Pinto " "
⊗⊗	†. es. 22 hp.	Chas. E. Brown	Young " "	Belknap " "
⊗⊗	⚓ }	J. W. McComb	Jack " "	Jacksboro " "
⊗⊗ m	⊞A+ }	" " "	" " " " "	" "
⊗⊗	∪. Either side.	W. G. Vineon	Choctaw Nt B17	Gainesville " "
⊗⊗	⟁ side. X sh. }	A. J. Addington	Wild Horse Creek "	" " " "
⊗⊗	⟁ " X " }	" " "	" " " " "	" " " "
⊗⊗	⟁ side & hip	John Flint	Young Co Texas	Fort Worth " "
⊗⊗ m	♡→ right side			
⊗⊗	♡→ " " }	J K P Shirley	Palo Pinto " "	Palo Pinto " "
⊗⊗	♡→ r " B sh.			
⊗⊗	♡→ " " Sh.			

Ear Marks.	BRANDS.	NAME.	RANCHE.	POST OFFICE.
	⟋Δ	F. J. Waite	Paul's Valley B.I.T	Paul's Valley, B.I.T
	+L	J. N. Morrison	Akle. Co. Texas	Colorado City, Texas
	◇ l. side.			
	◇ l. side.			
	Δ	Matthew Cartwright	Stonewall & Kaufman Co.	Terrall, Texas
	♡ R. corner.			
Horses	♡			
	≡ s. l. n.			
	—6	B. J. Addlington	B I T	Gainesville "
	+O+	Wm Harris		
	+G. Es.	H. Scott	Colorado & Pecos Rivers	Colorado City "
	♡ left side	J. W. McKenzie	Andrews Co Tex	" " "
	⌀	" "	" " "	Erin Springs "
	☧ left side Various places	W. H. Williams	B I T	" " "
	⌐	" "	" "	" " "
	⋀ across back from	J. M. Jones.	Clay. Co. Tex.	Riverland Texas.
	one side cattle	Arlington Cattle Co.	Nolan " "	Burnett " "

96

Ear Marks.	BRANDS.	NAME.	RANCHE.	POST OFFICE.
	⊲H .x.s.			
	⊲H .b.s.			
	F. E. Scrhip.			
	F. W. Phip			
	⊲H E.S.	A. P. Bush Jr	Scurry Co Texas	Colorado City Texas
	⊲H			
Horse	⊲H .e.hip.			
	YA some times only one ear			
	◻P X			
	⊐	J. W. Knox.	Jack Co Texas	Jacksboro " "
	◇	J. M. Jones	Clay " "	Riverland "
	P. Vork			
	⊏ork	J. F. Evans	Donley " "	Sherman "
	⊏ V			
	◇			
	◊ ◊	Curtis & Atkinson	Panhandle	Henrietta "

97

Ear Marks.	BRANDS.	NAME.	RANCHE.	POST OFFICE.
	H			
	+			
	I b S	J. N. Simpson	Baylor. Co. Tex.	Dallas Texas.
	I S th			
	I St Louis			
	I L th			
	U bS. th.	Matador Cattle Co	Ballard Spring	Fort Worth "
	A			
	△			
	♡	J. D. Reed	Camp Supply B I T.	Fort Worth "
	#			

98

Ear Marks.	BRANDS.	NAME.	RANCHE.	POST OFFICE.
	◇ l. sh.	C. C. Slaughter	Colorado River	Dallas Texas.
	I any place	J. N. Simpson	Baylor Co Tex	" " "
	△ l.s. OO.rs.			
	△ left hip.	A. L. Butler	Clay " "	Henrietta "
	HC l.s. OO.rs.			
	—3 l. oin			
	∩ s. th. or h	Guthreville L. Mattea	Hardeman " "	Gainesville "
	—L. l.s.	For particulars	see Figure brands.	
	⊥	W. B. Worsham	Hardeman Co Tex.	Henrietta "
	STV		to F. P. Ernest.	
	3200. head yearling & 2 year old steers. sold		Deer Trail Colorado.	
	⊞ left s.	W. H. Williams	B I T	Erie Springs B I T
	† r.h.r.s. l. sh.	" " "	"	" " "
	◁ E. l. side			
	—.s. AGn	G. M. Casey	See Next page	Clinton Mo
	R. hip.			
	⫼ . hip.			

99

Ear Marks.	BRANDS.	NAME.	RANCHE.	POST OFFICE.
	Q Q ! side		G. M. Casey, Represents	
	◇ . "	G. M Casey	Champion Cattle Co.	Clinton Mo
	H "		& Colorado. Mitchell	" "
	⊥ . (Ths) (one has been stolen)		" Texas. & the	" "
	♡ 7 .		Concho Cattle Co.	" "
	♡ 7 .		Coleman City Tex	" "
	◇ r.s.	Tom Montgomery	Kent Co.	Fort Worth Texas
Horses	⊕ (hip)	L. S. Williams	I. T.	Spanish Fort
	¥ side	Glasgow Caney & Co.	Young Co	Graham
	4 ls. Snych	W. B. Gardner	Deckins & Young	Albany "
	4 ls ∃ rs.			
	(alius)	Willcaye	Wol. mt. Fork	Colorado "
	K s L w	Milliken		Weatherford
	? ls. ◊ th	B. R. Coff	Clay Co.	Henrietta "
	⋈ ci. s.	Hanson Ward & Byler	see ⋈ ♡ brand for particulars	
	(hip) side) sho	Lindsay Bedford & Hicks	Cottle Co.	Benjamin "

Ear Marks.	BRANDS.	NAME.	RANCHE.	POST OFFICE.
⬭⬭	X lor. X ju.			
⬭⬭	⌶ lo. br.			
⬭⬭	◇F r.s.	Franklin	Greer Co.	Doans
Horses	◇F lhip.	Lana ᵐᵃ		Wilbarger Texas
⬭⬭	☐ ls.	Cattle Co.		
⬭⬭	A2 bs.	W. S. Power	Fisher Co.	Sweetwater "
⬭⬭	◻ r.r.b.s.	J. B. Elliew	Childress "	Kirkland "
⬭⬭	ꟻD r.s.	W. H. Yarbrough	Red River	Burlington "
⬭⬭	△ ls.			
⬭⬭	△ ls. OO r.s.	A. L. Butler	Clay Co.	Henrietta "
⬭⬭	△ ls. ▽ lr.			
⬭⬭	ꟼ l.sh. ᵃ a.b.sh.	A Silverstein	Crosby "	Wallas "
⬭⬭	ꟼ ꟼ ls.			
⬭⬭	ꟼ	G. W. Williams	Pecos R.	Lookout N. M.
⬭⬭	ꟼꟼ	J. H. Wilson	Montague	Spanish Fort. Texas
⬭⬭	ꟼꟼ			

Ear Marks.	BRANDS.	NAME.	RANCHE.	POST OFFICE.
∞	+ - +	Wm. T. Scott		Coleman Texas
∞		Hopson End	Hardeman	Gainsville "
∞		Reynolds		
∞		C. M. Easley	Clay Co.	Henrietta "
∞		A. J. Addington	I. T.	Gainsville "
∞			Greer Co.	Doan "
∞		J. C. Legan + White		Graham "
∞		J. W. Knox	Jack "	Jacksboro "
∞				
∞				
∞	" - "	E. C. Sugg & Bro	I. T.	Gainsville "
∞				
∞				
∞		Curtis + Atkinson	Panhandle	Henrietta "
∞		St Louis Cow Co	Lubbock Co	No 22 Clay Bldg St Louis
∞				
∞				

102

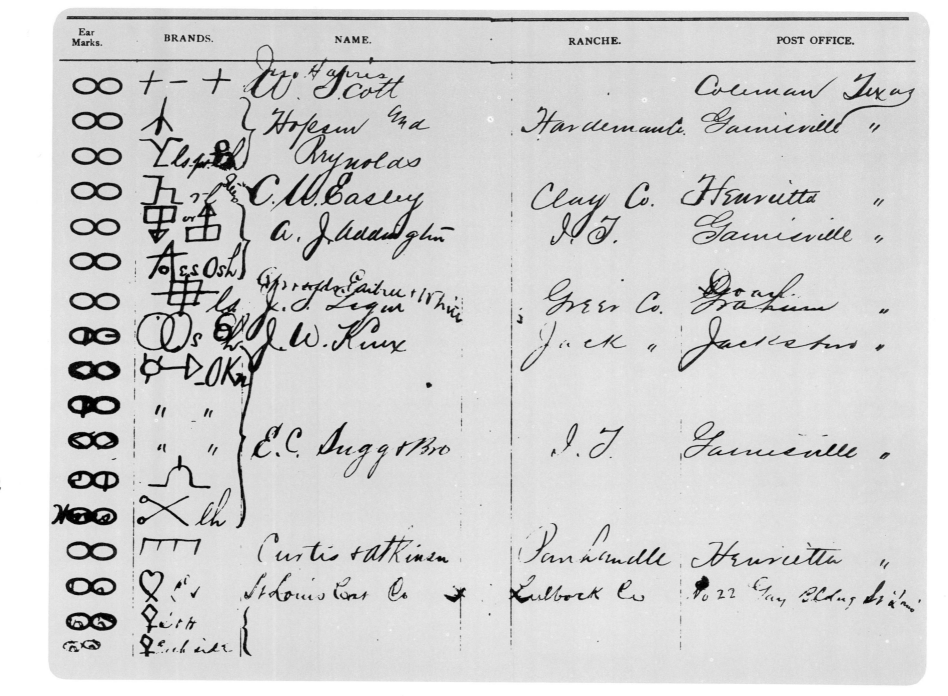

Ear Marks.	BRANDS.	NAME.	RANCHE.	POST OFFICE.
∞	⊟ LS 2 n			
∞	▽ . O ½	Mallett Cat	Colorado River	Colorado City
∞	▣	Company	¾ Morgan Co	Tex
∞	⊟	D.P. Atwood Mang		
∞	Shi Y hip O½	A. Lichenstein	Crosby Co	Dallas Tex
∞	⊤	Geo. H. Goddard		
∞	⊤ S & H			
∞	▷ s ⊤ h	Jno M. Hamilton	Chick Nat	Gainesville Tex
∞	▷ S l Y hip	Sold out of these		
∞	▷ S l Y h	800 1-2-3 steers to		
∞	▷ s	Hewin & Titus		
∞				
∞				
∞				
∞				
∞				

103

Ear Marks.	BRANDS.	NAME.	RANCHE.	POST OFFICE.
⊘⊘	6 P. Sth.	Hopson & Reynold	Cherokee Nt BIT	Gainesville Texas
⊘⊘	6 P. Sth.	some the cattle in first	brand sold to F. R. Harwood & now held in Panhandle
⊘⊘	80 Either S	" " " " last	" " " W. L. Rice " " " Chickasaw. Nt.
⊘⊘	1 9. side.	J. P. Addington	Beaver Creek BIT	Kansas City Mo
⊘⊘	96 "	" " "	" " " " " "
⊘⊘	74 Hip	L. Hearne		Belle Plain Texas
⊘ ⊠	7 es. — A.			
⊘⊘	222 es	J. S. Wade	Clay Co. Texas	Whitesboro " "
⊘⊘	7A. L.side			
⊘⊘	2J 2J	Wilson & Morris		
⊘	2J	E. L. Morris	Mud Creek BIT	Spanish Fort " "
⊘⊘	8 8			
⊘⊘	6666 L.side	S. B. Burnett	Wichita Co. Tex	Fort Worth " "
⊘⊘	6666 L. L.s.	most of these Cattle are	dehorned. there was sold in Nov 1883. about
⊘⊘	6666 E.s.	1000. steers to Quinlan	Montgomery & Co of Kansas City, for the Indian
⊘⊘		Contract. they were rebranded C + are	now held on Wachita & Canadian River B I T

104

Ear Marks	BRANDS.	NAME.	RANCHE.	POST OFFICE.
⊘⊘	☐ Left & hip. }	Geo. H. Goddard	Tom Green Co Tex	St Louis Mo
⊘⊘	☐ ... ☐ h. }	" "	" " " "	" " "
⊘⊘	4O esth.	Kit. Carter. Cattle. Co	Dickens & King " "	Seymour Texas
⊘⊘	96 esth.	Sam Cutbirth	Callahan " "	Belle Plain " "
⊘⊘	7777 is.	P. M. Burnett	Wichita " "	Henrietta " "
⊘⊘	7777 is. 9n.	50 others included in	6666 sale to Quinlan	Montgomery Co
⊘⊘	7Z	M. Skard	Archer Co Texas	Henrietta Texas
⊘⊘	80 ... }	Clay. M. Mann.	Kent & Borden " "	Colorado City "
⊘⊘	80 }	" " "	" " " "	" " "
⊘⊘	89 5 8th.	C. H. White	Greer " "	Jacksboro "
⊘⊘	7 both hips.	Adams & Holloway	Borden " "	Colorado City "
⊘⊘	7 Either side.	Forsythe Land & Cattle "	Cottle " "	Gainsville "
⊘⊘	96 9 side.	Espuela Cattle Co	N. W. Texas	Fort Worth "
⊘⊘	7L esth.			
⊘⊘	7L }	W. B. Slaughter	Crosby Co Texas	Dockums Ranche "
⊘⊘	7L 7L }			

Ear Marks.	BRANDS.	NAME.		RANCHE.	POST OFFICE.
∞	7 7 7 }	Glidden & Sanborn		Potter & Randall Co.	Houston Texas
∞	8 ∞ 8 }	For particulars		See Character brands.	
∞	7. side & neck }	E. C. Sugg & Bro		Beaver Creek Bit	Gainesville "
∞	2 = 2. side. 2	" " "		" " "	" " "
Horses ∞	8+ }				
Horses ∞	9C }	Joseph Campbell		Clay Co. Texas	Henrietta "
Horses ∞	N }				
∞	8.s. ∞ hip.	Louisville L. & Cattle Co		King " "	Seymour "
∞	8.bs. ∞ b.hips.	" " " "		" " " "	" " "
∞	2..Es. both.	J. L. Hull		Clay " "	Secret Springs "
∞	2D soot. 2.g.				
∞	2 D	J. J. Jackson		Coleman & Kent "	Coleman City "
∞	2 D				
Horses ∞	2 D. l.sh. }				
∞	5 5 5 5. bs.	Dan Waggoner & Son		North Texas 181+	Decatur " "
∞	6 Sh & h.	F. M. Hill		Collin Co Tex	McKinney " "

106

Ear Marks.	BRANDS.	NAME.	RANCHE.	POST OFFICE.
	2 K 2. es.	Chas. E. Brown	Young Co. Tex.	Belknap Texas
	5 side 5 hip.	A. E. Farrell	Cooke " "	Gainesville " "
	Z 7 7			
	Z 7 }	W. C. Wright	Cattle " "	Bolivar Denton co. " "
	7. eh 1th			
	Ork 77 side			
	0.. 77.. Ork.	E. W. Word	North Texas Dis	Kansas City. Mo.
	77..			
	77. rsth.			
	7. rs.	G. W. Williams	Pecos River	Dallas Texas
	777. rsth. }			
	172. es.	W. F. Lewis	Tom Green Co Tx	Colorado City " "
	7M. es.	H. A. Pierce	Howard " "	Waxahatchie " "
	7. es.	Geo. A Scaling	Kent " "	Hubbard City " "
	127 es			
	2 ♡. hrs. }	A. P. Bush Jr	Scurry " "	Colorado " " " "
	2 ♡ 2. s.			

107

Ear Marks.	BRANDS.	NAME.	RANCHE.	POST OFFICE.
	?sd. T. ?h.	Voith		
	?Either side & hips	Guinesville L & Cattle Co	Hardeman Co. Tex	Guinesville Texas
	?E scr. h.	Sold yearling steers 1883 to T. 8	Hutton & ranses his ranch now held in BIT. south of Hummewell	
		" 2 years " " " G. N.	Miller. " 101 " " " " " " "
	U8. {any place}	Arlington Cattle Co	Nolan " "	Burnett "
	2. Shoulder			
	7T+	J. M. Loving	Clay " "	Riverland "
	69	J. N. Simpson	Baylor " "	Dallas "
	1 sh. 50 h.			
	71. side.	Matador Cattle co	Ballard Spring	Fort Worth "
	71L			
	80			
	747	J. D. Reed	Camp Supply BIT. " " "	
	15 }	W. B. Worsham	Hardeman Co Tex	Henrietta "
	3 }	" " "	" " " "	" " "
	7Z. }	C. C. Slaughter	Colorado River	Dallas " "
	9. side }	" " "	" " " "	" " "

108

Ear Marks.	BRANDS.	NAME.	RANCHE.	POST OFFICE.
	7 X	Curtis & Atkinson	Panhandle	Henrietta Texas
	7	G. M. Casey	See Character	Clinton "
	3L. ls. }	M. T. Skard	Clay Co. Tex	Henrietta "
	O 2 }		" " " "	" " "
	O12. ls.	R. R. Milton	Archer " " "	Archer City "
	79. ls. }			
	97. ls. }	W. A. Williams	B I T	Erin Springs B I T
	97. R hip }			
	HL. }			
	96. }	Morris & Brown		Gainesville Texas
	B. }			
	5. ls & h. !! Jaw. }			
	5 left side }			
	5 hip. }	G. M. Casey	{For Particular See Character brands}	Clinton Mo
	K. hip. }			
	3 " }			

109

Ear Marks.	BRANDS.	NAME.	RANCHE.	POST OFFICE.
	3 Y. hip	G. M. Casey	{ see character	Clinton Mo
	3 V. "	" "	for particulars }	" "
	3 ls. 3 th			
	b.s.	B. R. Cobb	Clay Co.	Henrietta Tex.
	2 C loth	sold in 1803 out-	of COB—AOB—HB & brands	were rebranded O 2 O
	2 C loth	500 head steers to	Harris Bros	
	4 H B 95 LC	and are still held	in Cobbs pasture	
	10. 2 side	Cluck & Sparks	J. T.	Gainesville Tex.
	7 th side 7 th	L. S. Williams	"	Spanish Fort "
	4 trail cutter	J. R. Hudson	Holmer & Llano	Burnett "
	4 hip			
	4 X 4	Williams and	Old int fork	Weatherford
	4 4	Milliken		Colorado "
	12 r s th			
	5 l.s. head	Glasgow Causey & Co.	Young Co.	Graham "
	7 X S ls			

110

Ear Marks.	BRANDS.	NAME.	RANCHE.	POST OFFICE.
⊖⊖	8 sh.h. &s	A. L. Butter	Clay Co.	Henrietta Texas
⊖⊖	" "			
⊖⊖	3 h.h.s. 3h.	J. H. Shue	" "	" "
⊖⊖	7 D l.s.	J. B. Wilson	Cncho "	Wallus "
⊖⊖	7 D "			
⊖⊖	2 U h.r.s.	M. S. Power	Fisher Co.	Sweetwater "
⊖⊖	7 X b.s.			
⊖⊖	J 66 r.s.	W. A. Garner	Palo Pinto Co.	Ft. Worth "
⊖⊖	10 r.h.			
⊖⊖	2 O l.s. h	C. M. Tilford	Crosby "	Colurado "
⊖⊖	30 " "			
⊖⊖	4	J. B. Wilson	Crosby "	Wallus "
⊖⊖	3 T s Ocypher	J. L. Hull	Clay Co	Henrietta "
⊖⊖	4 T s Ocypher			
⊖⊖	4 l.s. Wj.	R. R. Wade	North Cncho	Colurado "
⊖⊖	4		Tom Green Co.	

111

Ear Marks.	BRANDS.	NAME.	RANCHE.	POST OFFICE.
	5 ×.5.	Tom Montgomery	Kent Co.	Fort Worth Texas
Horses	5 ch.			
	2 ÷ 2 .			
	80 ×.5.	E. C. Sugg	I. T.	Gainesville "
	7			
	7X 7X	Curtis & Atkinson	Panhandle	Henrietta "
	7D			
	78 es.el	W. H. Williams	I. T.	Erie Springs I.T.
	2 0 2 ×.5.	Creighton Co. & Co	Garza Co	Fort Worth T..
	2 0 2 's + 6			
	2 0 2 's B.			
	2 L P	Mallett Cattle	Colorado River	Colorado City "
	2 side strip	Co		
	2 ~ Sa. Tom			
	7 Z	M. Kade	Archer Co.	Henrietta ...
	2 Z	J. R. Gladney .	B.I.T.	Buff/creek I.T..

112

Ear Marks.	BRANDS.	NAME.	RANCHE.	POST OFFICE.
⌒⌒	101	Geo. H. Goddard		
∞	80			
◐◑	88 s (shelly)	S. J. Gavin	Washita R.	White Bear Hill 2½
◐◑	7L any	R.B. down left Sh		
∞				
8				
8				
8				
8				
8				
8				
8				
8				
8				
8				

INDEX

116

117

Presidio Live Stock Co.: 85
Putnam, A., Jr.: 62

Quinlan Montgomery & Co.: 44

Randall County, Texas: 6, 11, 28, 68, 78, 94, 106
Rayner, W. E.: 15, 17, 39, 46, 61, 84
Red River: 10, 13, 101
Red River Cattle Co.: 14, 27, 36, 54, 64, 67, 70, 82, 88, 91
Reed, J. D.: 12, 30, 34, 45, 61, 65, 76, 78, 98, 108
Rennie, James: 93
Reynolds: S. F.: 19, 30, 40, 57, 62
Riverland, Texas: 30, 88, 96, 97, 108
Roanoke, Texas: 19, 27, 30, 40, 57, 62
Rodgers, W. A.: 20
Roff, A. B.: 26, 36, 64, 72, 74, 82, 93
Rumsill, C. C.: 14, 64
Running Water: 60
Rush Creek: 93

Sacra & Sugg: 10, 22, 42, 46
St. Louis Cattle Co.: 9, 32, 43, 60, 66, 79, 85, 90, 102
St. Louis, Missouri: 9, 14, 23, 32, 60, 66, 92, 105
San Saba River, Texas: 93
Scaling, George A.: 7, 12, 26, 107
Schumding, Charles: 9, 32, 60, 66
Scott, W.: 17, 39, 74, 78, 86, 96, 102
Scurry County, Texas: 7, 12, 21, 24, 39, 43, 45, 49, 52, 57, 74, 80, 84, 87, 89, 90, 97, 107
Secret Springs Texas: 14, 21, 47, 64, 68, 74, 87
Seymour, Texas: 6, 12, 14, 15, 17, 21, 23, 24, 36, 37, 39, 40, 41, 44, 45, 46, 52, 56, 61, 63, 64, 65, 67, 68, 74, 76, 83, 84, 92, 94, 105
Sherman, Texas: 15, 16, 31, 40, 43, 46, 52, 54, 57, 72, 75, 76, 80, 87, 91, 97
Sherwood, F. R.: 54, 104
Shirley J. K. P.: 95
Silverstein, A.: 101, 103
Simpson, J. N.: 7, 8, 10, 13, 21, 24, 30, 40, 42, 50, 62, 65, 69, 70, 78, 80, 98, 99, 108
Slaughter, C. C.: 8, 13, 15, 21, 30, 40, 46, 50, 58, 60, 69, 75, 99, 108
Slaughter, J. B.: 50, 78
Slaughter, W. B.: 6, 15, 23, 28, 78, 79, 83, 90, 94, 105
Smith & Forsythe: 55
Spanish Fort, Texas: 9, 16, 34, 42, 46, 54, 57, 72, 77, 83, 92, 100, 101, 104, 110
Stephens County, Texas: 19, 21, 68, 74
Stephenville, Texas: 23,33, 79, 94
Stine, J. H., & Bros.: 51, 70
Stone, John H.: 12, 21, 74
Stonewall County, Texas: 5, 6, 7, 27, 28, 36, 38, 45, 49, 55, 61, 68, 72, 83, 89, 95, 96
Stradley, J. H.: 40, 76
Strawn Texas: 21, 74
Strue, J. H., & Bros.: 77, 111
Sugg, E. C.: 112
Sugg, E. C., & Bro.: 33, 34, 50, 56, 60, 66, 77, 94, 102, 106
Sweeney, D. B.: 47
Sweeney, D. H.: 44
Sweetwater Creek, Texas: 24
Sweetwater, Texas: 22, 24, 32, 33, 41, 43, 60, 62, 66, 70, 77, 81, 85, 88, 101, 111

118

Swenson, E. P.: 67

Tackitt, L. L.: 29, 45
Tarrant County, Texas: 31, 53
Taylor, J. W.: 29
Terrell, Texas: 7, 49, 83, 96
Thorp Springs, Texas: 18
Throckmorton County, Texas: 75, 90
Tilford, C. M.: 17, 71, 86, 111
Tom Green County, Texas: 14, 23, 29, 38, 49, 78, 82, 83, 92, 105, 107
Turner, Lancaster & Co.: 49
Tuttle, W. W.: 55, 68, 72

Vaden, H. L.: 19, 81
Valley View, Texas: 5, 12, 45, 48, 72, 87
Vernon, Texas: 72, 93
Vinson, W. G.: 12, 38, 95

Wade, R. R.: 85, 111
Wade, T. S.: 11, 14, 27, 33, 54, 82, 92, 104
Waggoner, Dan, & Son: 12, 18, 28, 68, 83, 95, 106
Waite, F. T.: 87, 96
Washington, J. C.: 42, 59, 71, 77
Washita, R.: 17, 77, 113
Waxahachie, Texas: 52, 74, 107
Weatherford, Texas: 8, 27, 32, 41, 49, 51, 66, 70, 76, 100, 110
White Bear Hill: 17, 77, 83, 93, 113
White, G. H.: 5, 21, 105
Whitesboro, Texas: 11, 14, 27, 33, 54, 92, 104
Wichita & Brazos Stock Assn.: 47
Wichita County, Texas: 6, 44, 55, 72, 104, 105
Wichita Falls, Texas: 6
Wilbarger, Texas: 101
Wild Horse Creek, Texas: 95
Williams, G. W.: 24, 26, 49, 59, 83, 101, 107
Williams, L. S.: 16, 46, 100, 110
Williams, W. H.: 12, 29, 31, 57, 76, 84, 96, 99, 109, 112
Wilson, J. A.: 72, 93
Wilson, J. B.: 20, 41, 47, 51, 59, 111
Wilson, J. W.: 19, 57, 62, 84
Wilson, T. H.: 34, 101
Wilson, T. H., & Bro.: 57, 83
Wilson & Morris: 34, 54, 57, 72, 83, 104
Wise County, Texas: 41, 67, 93
Witherspoon: 28, 68
Witherspoon, J. G.: 94
Witherspoon, P. S.: 94
Wolcott, G. W.: 38, 83
Word, C. W.: 18, 24, 78, 107
Worsham, W. B.: 13, 34, 57, 62, 65, 69, 81, 87, 99, 108
Wright, W. C.: 107

Yarborough, W. H.: 9, 10, 13, 42, 77, 101
Young County, Texas: 5, 12, 18, 20, 23, 25, 26, 28, 29, 31, 36, 38, 43, 45, 47, 49, 50, 52, 56, 57, 59, 74, 77, 82, 84, 89, 92, 95, 107, 110
Young, J. B.: 93
Zook, J. W.: 23, 52, 92